Dr. Wright's
Kitchen Table Math

A Step-by-step Guide
For Teaching Your Child Math

Book 3
Elementary School Math
Beyond Arithmetic

Equations and Inequalities, Word Problems,
Statistics, Probability, Graphing, Geometry,
Measurements, Time, Money, and Reasoning

Chris Wright, Ph.D.

The CSBD Publishing Group

Published by: The CSBD Publishing Group
                1402 Eolus Ave
                Encinitas, CA 92024-1732
                (760) 436-8703

Book website: www.DrWrightsKitchenTableMath.com

ISBN-13: 978-0-9829211-1-1

Cover design: Becky Wright, Chris Wright, and Sarah Wright
Cover photo and sketch: Becky Wright

Photos & illustrations: Becky Wright, Chris Wright, Whitney Sundby, Renée Espinoza, and Adrienne Espinoza.
Tiling pattern: Danny Wright.

Printed in the United States of America.

First Printing 2010.

About This Book

This book continues the mathematical exploration that your child started in the first two books of this series. The first book developed your child's mathematical abilities, from understanding quantities, to working with numbers, to doing arithmetic with single-digit numbers. The second book developed your child's talents for doing arithmetic with fractions and multi-digit numbers.

This third book describes how to teach your child elementary school mathematics beyond the core arithmetic skills. It has chapters on geometry, equations, word problems, probability, statistics, graphing, time, and money. Although each chapter in this book assumes mastery of appropriate chapters in the first two books, it is possible, and even desirable, to skip back and forth between all three books.

The steps are presented here in a logical order, but let your child and opportunity also serve as guides. Take advantage of your special one-on-one tutoring situation with your child to follow a course dictated more by interest and fun, and less by how it happens to be laid out in a book or in school.

Our approach

This book is born out of my wife's and my experiences with our two children, as well as my experiences working with a great many other young children. The purpose of this book is to provide parents with a series of clear, easy-to-do steps and activities that illustrate the methods of basic mathematics and help develop a child's mathematical skills. The book provides detailed information for each step so that parents have all that they will need to teach the step. There are explanations, examples, practice ideas, related activities, and games.

This book provides a structure and a methodology for understanding numbers and for developing number sense. It provides mental models and techniques that can be used to emphasize learning mathematical structures and relationships rather than simple, tedious memorization of procedures that involve little understanding.

Many parents reading this book will be first-time teachers of mathematics. In describing the steps, I have tried to help parents avoid some of the traps or pitfalls that may happen the first time someone works with this material. I have filled in all of the intermediate steps so that everything is explained. I also show how some steps depend on other steps.

Parents should not be concerned about repeating, or even pre-empting, what their child learns in school, as children benefit from repetition and take pleasure in it (to a point). The steps given in this book introduce concepts that need to be repeated and reinforced many times in different contexts before they are fully grasped. Most of the material can be practiced with your child doing everyday things.

Working through the steps in this book

Each chapter offers a number of steps to introduce and teach a particular skill. Many of these skills are related, so please jump around among the chapters as may seem fun or appropriate with your child. Follow your interests and skip around between this book and other books in this series, and do not worry if you do not seem to be presenting the activities in a controlled or logical way.

Children's learning is rarely predictable and tidy. For each child there will be opportunities or needs that suggest doing things in certain sequences. A big advantage you have working individually with your child is being able to custom tailor the learning experience.

Where there is no dependency between steps, there is no reason not to try doing more than one step at a time. At times it is nice for the child to have another idea to learn and play with while one idea is sinking in. Also, giving a choice of math activities allows your child to choose something that happens to feel like more fun at the time, and gives a greater sense of involvement.

It is best to let your child seek out his or her own readiness level naturally and spontaneously. Normal, healthy children have different physical and mental timetables for development. Pushing your child in the hope that this will speed things up is fruitless and may frustrate your child, or even set your child back because of feelings of discouragement. Be willing to switch to a different step, and drop an activity temporarily, if your child does not seem ready or interested. You may find that the activity may be perfectly suited to your child the following week or month.

Learning through problem solving

Use problem solving as a way to learn new things whenever possible. Introduce new subjects or games by giving your child example problems or situations to figure out. Pick these problems carefully to put your child on a path of guided discovery.

Take the subject of solving a one-step equation from Chapter 1: *Equations and Inequalities* as an example. This could be introduced by showing your child each of the four types of equations, one for each kind of operation, and then having your child memorize and practice the method for solving each type. Instead of that, start by looking at simple equations that your child can do easily. Go through examples with small numbers so that your child can solve the problems intuitively or using manipulatives. After figuring out quite a few of these problems of increasing difficulty, combined with some guided learning from you, most children will figure out the general rules on their own.

Learning through problem solving has many advantages. When your child discovers how something works, important connections are made with associated material in ways that are impossible to create through merely being told something. Problem solving engages your child in the learning process, changing your child from a passive learner into an active learner. Most importantly, problem solving is a critical skill vital throughout life, quite independent of mathematics.

The degree to which you can use problem solving to teach a new subject will vary with the subject. Teaching measurement systems is mostly a matter of showing your child how to do things. A subject such as 2-digit adding can be guided by using a lot of examples with manipulatives, but in the end it will mostly be a matter of your showing your child how it works. As the topics become more advanced, there will be more opportunities for using problem solving. The chapters on counting, reasoning, and equations have many sections that can be taught this way.

 From time to time you will see a crossed-out parrot symbol. These are places that are tempting to teach by having your child memorize a rule or mechanical process. The extra effort required to understand why the ideas work, and learn how to apply the ideas, will be richly rewarded—the material will be more interesting and easier to remember, it will be better integrated with associated material, and your child will be able to apply the ideas more flexibly and powerfully.

Encourage your child to explore and wrestle with complicated problems, and do not be afraid to ask a question your child cannot answer. Learning to tackle complicated problems is an important ability, and it will not be learned if every question is answered in a single step that follows easily from the material you were just looking at.

If your child does not see how to go about doing a question, use it as an opportunity to work on problem solving skills. Ask your child if there are any ways to turn this problem into one worked on before. Also, suggest creating similar simpler problems, so that solving the simpler problems may lead to ideas on how to solve the original problem. Celebrate partial answers or ideas, even if they are wrong or do not solve the entire problem.

As you go through the various topics in this book, use a sense of exploration. Let your child discover things, rather than describing how they are done in advance. Let your child find different ways of doing things than you were expecting. Discuss, without any sense of which may be better or worse, the many ways some things can be done. Describe to your child everyday situations that require mathematical analysis, and watch your child solve these problems and develop ideas as they are needed.

Thoughts on teaching your child math

You may feel anxious about introducing your child to activities involving multi-digit arithmetic—these ideas may seem too complex and formidable for your young child. If you feel this way, try your best not to let it show. Introduce new steps as you would introduce a fun, new game.

To a child these activities are just different ways to play with numbers, and your child will not enter into the activity with any anxiety if you do not signal it in advance. Try to avoid saying things like, "Here comes the tricky part." You will be amazed at the number of times your child will be able to do things right off that you thought might be hard.

My wife and I remember enjoying numbers and having fun with them as children, and we have tried to share this pleasure with our children as well as to include it here in this book. If you do not have fond memories of working with numbers, please resist telling your child about it. If you say things like, "That's OK; I was never very good at math either," you are tempting your child to follow your lead. Imagine if someone said to a child, "That's OK; I was never very good at reading either."

When your child makes mistakes, use that as an opportunity to see which concepts have been confused, need reinforcing, or have been forgotten, and use it to direct your teaching. If something has not been grasped after repeated tries, don't look at it as your child failing. Either your child is not ready, the approach needs to be changed, or some background is missing. Use the situation to gain insights on how to teach better, never as a reason to be hard on your child.

Teaching is one of the best ways to learn something and to see how well you understand it. Every once in a while, pick a topic your child knows quite well and have your child teach it to you, as though you were a beginner. This teaching should include why things are done the way they are, in addition to how things are done. Areas where the explanations and descriptions stumble are good places to go back and review.

One of the more important aspects of this process is to do a few minutes of practice almost every day. There are two advantages to regular practice, when not done in excess. Consistent practice improves your child's proficiency, which creates a sense of accomplishment and an enthusiasm for the task. Also, if practice is a regular activity, it becomes an expected and accepted part of the day, which makes it easier for everyone.

Mix into this daily practice occasional review of material already mastered. In particular, if your child starts to stumble on some of the basic math facts, do a quick practice of these about once or twice a week until these are easy again. Your child should have effortless use of these facts so that they do not get in the way of working with more advanced topics.

More than anything, however, learning should be enjoyable. To a small child, learning and "work" are indistinguishable from "play." I hope that you and your child will share many happy hours of number play, as well as word and fantasy and paint and mud play, and that it will be a rewarding and memorable experience for both of you.

Please write

If you have any questions, new methods to suggest, or just want to chat about math education, please drop me a note. Contact me through my web site at `www.DrWrightsKitchenTableMath.com`. I would love to hear from you.

Chris Wright

Acknowledgements

A great many people have helped me during the 18-year span of this project.

My heartfelt thanks to:

My mother and father, for nurturing and supporting my love of mathematics, and especially my mother for the many hours proofreading early drafts.

My wife, Sarah, for all of her love and support through the years, and my children, Becky and Danny, for being my main guinea pigs and for sharing so many wonderful math times with me.

My brother, Larry, his wife, Mimi, and their children, Melissa and Laura, for providing the motivation for the original four pages of notes that became this series of books.

My many good math teachers, especially among them Molly Robinson for her friendship and her careful reading of a draft of this book.

The many children with whom I have had the privilege and pleasure of doing math.

The many parents who were nice enough to use early drafts of this book with their families.

The folks who helped me with illustrations, principally my daughter Becky, who had ideas and drawings for things I was hopeless at, and Whitney Sundby for her many excellent illustrations.

The good people at the Art of Problem Solving: Richard Rusczyk for offering to publish this book, and for his many helpful suggestions for editing and improving it, Dave Patrick for solving many an intractable LaTeX problem and his wonderful editing help, Maria

Monks and Ken G. Monks for the use of their METAPOST macros and figures, and Vanessa Rusczyk for her initial design for the page layout.

Several families who graciously provided family photographs throughout this book: the Underdahl family—Grace, Carrie, and Rees; the Espinoza family—Renée, Joe, Adrienne, Josey and Beth; Molly Lüthi and nieces Luca and Nico Jacobs; and of course my own Wright family—Danny, Becky, and Sarah.

Jenifer Robinson for many thoughtful discussions from her careful reading of a draft of this book, and to Gayle Robinson and her store, *Critical Thinkers*, for her wonderful support of the Kitchen Table Math series of books.

This book was produced using the MiKTeX installation of pdflatex, which is based on the LaTeX document processing system. My thanks to its many authors, and also to the authors of the specialized packages which were used to produce this book. The geometric diagrams were produced using the graphics language METAPOST. The pictures were edited using Adobe Photoshop and Illustrator.

Contents

3   Reasoning   52

4   Probability and Counting   64

5   Statistics and Graphing   87

6 Geometry 99

7 Measurements 161

8 Money 182

9 Manipulatives 192

10 Learning Games and Activities 202

CHAPTER 1

Equations and Inequalities

This chapter describes ways to gently introduce the idea of solving equations and finding the values of unknown quantities. The chapter starts off with two sections on verbal puzzles that you and your child can give each other. These puzzles are equations in disguise.

The next two sections begin the transition to written problems. They use blank spaces or letter substitution puzzles to accustom your child to working with unknowns. Letter substitution puzzles are used as first examples of using variables for unknowns. The idea of substituting a single digit for a single letter is easily understandable for most children, and it is less abstract and intimidating than solving for a variable in an equation.

After this progression of warm-up sections, one-step equations are introduced. These equations require one arithmetic step to solve. Your child will learn to use reverse operations to make these equations easy to solve. The use of reverse operations will be carried further for two-step equations a couple of sections later.

This is a good time to start doing word problems with your child, so you may want to start going through the material in Chapter 2: *Word Problems*. Word problems are a natural source of equations, so practicing them will show the usefulness of learning how to solve equations.

The second half of the chapter is a significant step up in sophistication from the first half. Be patient and make sure that your child has thoroughly mastered all of the skills in the first half of the chapter before moving on to this material. If your child has some significant problems with this new material, consider waiting 6 to 12 months before attempting it again. The ability to handle increased levels of abstraction and working with symbols in place of numbers is a developmental step—it cannot be rushed.

The next three sections cover skills needed to solve two-step equations. The first of these describes the order used to evaluate complex mathematical expressions. These rules are needed for deciding the order to use for solving two-step equations. There is a section on working with the distributive property, which is a property often needed when working with more complex expressions. The process of solving two-step equations is described as peeling an onion—reverse operations are used to peel back the onion one layer at a time to discover the value of the variable.

After that there are two sections describing basic ways to organize and clean up equations. The first step is to consolidate the variables on each side of an equation. The second section shows how to take variables on both sides of an equation, and move them all to one side.

The chapter then covers the most basic case of having several variables in several equations. This section introduces the idea of substitution, which means replacing a quantity by something that is equal to it. The idea is to get rid of the extra variables by using substitution.

The last section on equations covers solving proportions. Proportions occur frequently in ratio and rate problems, and also in geometry scaling problems. Proportions involve equations of a particular kind, and I describe a couple of methods for solving them.

After all of this work on equations, the last section of the chapter discusses inequalities. It starts off by describing the various kinds of inequalities, and how they can be displayed on a number line. It then talks about how inequalities can be solved using exactly the same techniques your child has learned to solve equations.

1.1   I'm thinking of a number

LESSON   Learning about beginning equations using verbal puzzles.

GAME   I'm Thinking of a Number: One person says he is thinking of a number. That person then says a mathematical clue concerning his number. For example, "When I add 15 to my number I get 29—what is my number?"

Practice▷   **Use reverse operations** Continuing the example in the game description above, we want to find the number for, "when I add 15 to my number I get 29." To reverse the adding of 15, you should subtract 15. So the number must be 29 − 15 = 14.

Encourage your child to check the answer by putting it back in the original problem. In this case, check the answer by verifying that 14 + 15 = 29.

Silly names Introduce the use of variable names by making the following change to the game. Tell your child that you are getting tired of referring to your number as "my number" or "the number I am thinking of." Say that you want to make it shorter, and to name it after something. Pick any silly name you want—the name of a doll, a friend, or whatever.

Now the game becomes—"I'm thinking of a number called Pluto. When I subtract 34 from Pluto I get 22. What is Pluto?"

Switch roles, play anywhere Switch roles with your child from time to time. Having your child ask the questions to challenge you is not only fun for your child, but the forming of the question, and checking to make sure that you get the right answer, leads to a better understanding of the whole process.

This game, and the bag game introduced in the next section, are great games to play in the car, bus, or train as you take the kids on various errands and activities.

1.2 The bag game

LESSON | Solving more complicated equations using verbal puzzles.

The bag game is an idea of educator Rick Garlikov, and is a variation of "I'm Thinking of a Number" that allows for trickier problems.

> **GAME** **Bag Game:** The game always starts off with "I have a bag and you have a bag ...". This is followed by some information about how the two bags are related. For example, you might say, "Our bags have the same number of things, and together we have 30." At the end always comes the question, "How many are in my bag and how many are in your bag?"

 You can make the bag game variations as tricky as your child can handle. As your child gets more involved, let your child invent the questions sometimes.

Some more examples are: "You have twice as much in your bag as I do, but if I add 12 more to mine we have the same," and, "You have 3 times as much in your bag as I do, but if I double mine and add 12 more, I will have twice as much as you do."

1.3   Using blank spaces

LESSON   Solving equations that have blank spaces.

Practice▷   **Blank spaces** A good introduction to solving equations without using variables is to use underlined blank spaces in the problems.
For example, fill in the blanks for

$$\_\_ + 23 = 59 \qquad\qquad 59 - \_\_ = 23$$

A child can get accustomed to seeing this sort of thing by
first practicing with straightforward calculation problems of the
form

$$43 + 24 = \_\_ \qquad\qquad 212 - 105 = \_\_$$

After practicing these simpler problems, it will not seem very
different to see problems such as $\_\_ + 3 = 9$ for the first time.

Checking work A nice thing about using blank spaces is that your
child can fill in the blank space with the answer, and then immediately see whether the answer makes sense in the whole
problem. For example, if your child fills in $\underline{35} + 23 = 59$, the
mistake will probably be obvious.

Single-digit blanks A variation of these puzzles is done using underlined spaces to represent a single digit in a multi-digit problem.
Create these by starting with a problem with all of the digits,
and then remove a few of the digits. Check the problem before
giving it to your child, to make sure you did not remove too
many digits!

$$
\begin{array}{ccccc}
23 & & \_3 & & 2\_ \\
+\ 36 & \implies & +\ 3\_ & \text{or} & +\ 36 \\
\hline
59 & & 59 & & \_9
\end{array}
$$

$$
\begin{array}{ccc}
17 & & 1\_ \\
\times\ 56 & & \times\ \_6 \\
\hline
102 & \implies & \_\_2 \\
+85 & & 1\ \_5 \\
\hline
952 & & \_\_\_
\end{array}
$$

1.4 Letter substitution puzzles

LESSON | Learning how to solve letter substitution puzzles.

Practice ▶

A letter substitution puzzle is an arithmetic problem in which some, or all, of the digits have been replaced by letters. They have three rules.

1. A letter represents the same single digit throughout a problem.

2. Different letters represent different digits.

3. No number can have a "0" for its leftmost digit.

The direct substitution of letters for numbers is easier for children to understand than solving traditional equations. They also are approached as more of a game.

Here are some problems for addition and multiplication. You can make subtraction and division problems out of these by reversing the arithmetic. For example, the addition problem $a + a = c4$ can be turned into $c4 - a = a$.

When making up your own puzzles, make them so that they have just one solution. If you get tired of creating puzzles, you can find some in mathematical games books.

$$
\begin{array}{r} 9 \\ + 4 \\ \hline a\,b \end{array}
\qquad
\begin{array}{r} a \\ + 5 \\ \hline 9 \end{array}
\qquad
\begin{array}{r} b \\ + 8 \\ \hline c \end{array}
\qquad
\begin{array}{r} b \\ + b \\ \hline 8 \end{array}
\qquad
\begin{array}{r} a \\ + a \\ \hline c\,4 \end{array}
\qquad
\begin{array}{r} a \\ + 2 \\ \hline b\,c \end{array}
\qquad
\begin{array}{r} d \\ + 2 \\ \hline c\,c \end{array}
$$

$$
\begin{array}{r} a \\ a \\ + a \\ \hline b\,2 \end{array}
\qquad
\begin{array}{r} c \\ c \\ + c \\ \hline d\,4 \end{array}
\qquad
\begin{array}{r} a \\ a \\ + 7 \\ \hline b \end{array}
\qquad
\begin{array}{r} a \\ a \\ + b \\ \hline b\,0 \end{array}
$$

$$
\begin{array}{r} a \\ + b \\ \hline a\,c \end{array}
\qquad
\begin{array}{r} a \\ + b\,b \\ \hline a\,7 \end{array}
\qquad
\begin{array}{r} b \\ + a\,b \\ \hline b\,a \end{array}
$$

7

$$
\begin{array}{r} b\,a \\ +\ b\,b \\ \hline c\,a\,b \end{array}
\qquad
\begin{array}{r} a\,d \\ +\ b\,d \\ \hline b\,c\,c \end{array}
\qquad
\begin{array}{r} a\,a \\ +\ b\,a \\ \hline b\,b\,c \end{array}
\qquad
\begin{array}{r} a\,a \\ +\ c\,b \\ \hline b\,b\,c \end{array}
\qquad
\begin{array}{r} a\,a \\ +\ a\,b \\ \hline c\,a\,c \end{array}
\qquad
\begin{array}{r} a\,a \\ +\ a\,a \\ \hline b\,b\,c \end{array}
$$

$$
\begin{array}{r} a\,b\,a \\ +\ a\,c\,a \\ \hline d\,d\,b\,b \end{array}
\qquad
\begin{array}{r} b\,a\,a \\ +\ c\,a\,a \\ \hline a\,b\,c \end{array}
$$

$$
\begin{array}{r} a \\ \times\ 4 \\ \hline 2\,8 \end{array}
\qquad
\begin{array}{r} d \\ \times\ 3 \\ \hline e\,7 \end{array}
\qquad
\begin{array}{r} f \\ \times\ f \\ \hline f \end{array}
\qquad
\begin{array}{r} b \\ \times\ 7 \\ \hline c\,b \end{array}
\qquad
\begin{array}{r} h \\ \times\ h \\ \hline 3\,h \end{array}
$$

1.5 One-step equations

LESSON | Learning to solve one-step equations.

Practice ▷ **Rule** In solving equations there is one golden rule that must always be observed.

> **RULE** Whatever is done to one side of an equation must be done to the other side.

Strategy There are three goals to keep in mind when solving most equations.

1. Clean up and simplify the equation.
2. Reverse, or undo, what is being done to the variable.
3. Get the variable by itself.

The first goal, cleaning up and simplifying the equation, is discussed in Section 1.9: *Simplifying equations*. The equations in this section will already be in a simplified form.

Reversing All of the equations for this step should be of the form: one operation is performed with a variable and a number, and the other side of the equation has a single number.

$$y + 127 = 812 \qquad\qquad x - 78 = 49$$
$$21 \times b = 861 \qquad\qquad c \div 5 = 51$$

Equations of the form $23 - a = 6$ and $36 \div b = 12$ take two steps to solve, so they are discussed in Section 1.8: *Two-step equations*.

Associated with the last two goals listed above are two questions that are useful in focusing your child's attention.

1. What is being done to the variable?
2. What needs to be done to the equation to get the variable by itself?

9

For one-step equations, if the reverse of what is being done to the variable is done to the equation, then the variable will be left by itself.

For example, in $y + 127 = 812$, y has 127 added to it. The reverse of adding 127 is to subtract 127. Subtracting 127 from both sides of the equation:

$$y + 127 - 127 = 812 - 127$$
$$y = 685$$

For another example, in $c \div 5 = 51$, c is being divided by 5. The reverse of dividing by 5 is multiplying by 5.

$$c \div 5 \times 5 = 51 \times 5$$
$$c = 255$$

Create a mystery One fun way to teach about reverse operations is to stage a mystery, perhaps pretending that some household item has been stolen.

Take dolls and place them near the place of the theft. By each doll put a card with a statement. Each statement will have the form: "After the theft took place I <a single action>." For example, the actions could be walking forward or backward some number of steps.

Your child will need to reverse the actions to figure out which doll was the one that was at the place where the theft happened.

Reversing multiplication by a fraction For the equation $\frac{2}{5}x = 12$, to undo the multiplication by $\frac{2}{5}$, you should divide by it. Dividing by $\frac{2}{5}$ is fine, but you can save a step by changing this into multiplying by the reciprocal, $\frac{5}{2}$. Use the rule: *dividing by a number is the same as multiplying by its reciprocal.*

Some children need the security of not deviating from the pattern of doing the reverse operation. For those children there is no reason to change. Other children will see that $\frac{2}{5} \times \frac{5}{2} = 1$ just as well as $\frac{2}{5} \div \frac{2}{5} = 1$, and they will be happy to save a step.

Showing work Some children are able to solve these problems in their head, without writing any work. The difficulty with this comes when they do problems that have 2, 3, or more steps. Have your child write out the steps at least some of the time, so the skill will be available for more complicated problems.

There are a number of ways to show the work in solving an equation. One way is to do it as shown in the previous examples.

Another popular approach is to write the change on the line below the equation. Below that, the final equation is written.

$$
\begin{array}{r}
y + 127 = 812 \\
-127 \quad -127 \\
\hline
y = 685
\end{array}
$$

My own favorite is a short-hand version of the first method. There is no advantage in showing the canceling on the side with the variable, so I often leave it out. But, it is nice to see what is happening on the other side, all of which can be done on one line:

$$y = 812 - 127 = 685$$

Creating problems Here is a simple way to create these problems.

Start with an operation you want your child to practice. Use the reverse of that operation to create the side of the equation with the variable. For example, start with $4x$ if you want to give your child practice solving division problems with 4, or start with $x - 8$ if you want to give practice with adding 8.

Next, substitute into your expression the solution you want for x. For example, if you want the solution to be 23, then calculate $4x = 4 \times 23 = 92$ or $x - 8 = 23 - 8 = 15$. This produces the problems $4x = 92$ and $x - 8 = 15$, both of which have the solution $x = 23$.

 RELATED

Practicing word problems is a great way for your child to see the usefulness of equations. Look at the material in Chapter 2: *Word Problems* for ways to work on word problems.

1.6 Order of operations

LESSON | Learning the order for performing operations.

Practice ▷   Your child is starting to work with more complicated mathematical expressions. There is a rule for how to make sense of something as complex as

$$(2 + 3)^2 - 6 \times 2 \div 3 + 2^3 \times [5 - 3]$$

What do you do first, and what comes next? The mnemonic device that students like to use is

Please Excuse My Dear Aunt Sally

The first letters of these words, PEMDAS, are the first letters for the order in which things should be done in a mathematical expression:

Parentheses Exponent Multiply Divide Add Subtract

Parentheses Any expression enclosed by a pair of parentheses, or by any grouping symbols, is evaluated first. In the above expression, that means turning (2 + 3) into 5, and [5 − 3] into 2. The expression then becomes

$$5^2 - 6 \times 2 \div 3 + 2^3 \times 2$$

Exponents Any expressions involving exponents are evaluated next. In the example, 5^2 is 25 and 2^3 is 8. So, the example becomes

$$25 - 6 \times 2 \div 3 + 8 \times 2$$

Multiplication and division Despite multiplication being listed before division, they have equal priority. If two or more multiplications and divisions are next to each other, they are performed from left to right. In $6 \times 2 \div 3$, that means that 6×2 is done first to make 12, and then $12 \div 3$ makes 4. Similarly, the 8×2 is done at this time to produce 16. The example now becomes

$$25 - 4 + 16$$

Addition and subtraction Addition and subtraction are done last. Similar to multiplication and division, these two operations have equal priority, and are done from left to right. The final answer for the example is:

$$25 - 4 + 16 = 21 + 16 = 37$$

Certainly, most of your child's problems will not be this complicated. However, the rules are important, and your child should get to the point of automatically knowing that $2 + 3 \times 5$ is 17, and not 25.

GAME **Parentheses Game**: Take an expression that is missing some parentheses, and challenge your child to find the right places to put parentheses to get the desired value. In this example the goal is to get 9, and the expression is:

$$2 + 7 \times 5 - 2 \times 2$$

One answer is:

$$(2 + 7) \times (5 - 2 \times 2)$$

Playing this game forces your child to think about the rules for which operations are done first, and how to change them by putting in parentheses to achieve the goal number. The problems are easy to create—start with an expression with parentheses in it and then remove them.

PEMDAS and GEMDAS I do not like the initials PEMDAS because not all grouping uses parentheses. In its place I like to use GEMDAS, with the G standing for grouping. Remember this as:

Graciously **E**xcuse **M**y **D**ear **A**unt **S**ally

1.7 Distributive property

LESSON | Learning about the distributive property.

Practice ⟶ This is a property that occurs frequently and is worth knowing by name. In some ways it is quite straightforward, but it presents some subtle potential pitfalls for your child.

 The *distributive property* says that if you multiply a number by the sum of two numbers, then that is the same as adding together the products of the separate multiplications.

For example, nine fives is the same as six fives and three fives:

$$(6 + 3) \times 5 = (6 \times 5) + (3 \times 5)$$

Here are couple of ways to illustrate this property to your child.

Arrays A good way of demonstrating distributivity is to represent multiplication with a rectangular array. In this array your child can see that 9 rows of 5 is the same as 6 rows of 5 together with 3 more rows of 5.

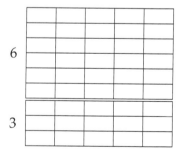

Bags Another way to demonstrate this idea is to talk about bags. Suppose you have a collection of bags, each of which has 5 apples. Having 9 bags with five apples is the same as having 6 bags with 5 apples together with 3 more bags with 5 apples.

Notice that the 5 apples have very little to do with the explanation. The main idea is that if you have 6 of something and 3 more of that thing, that is the same as having 9 of them. It is a simple idea when expressed in this way, but it can look complicated if the central theme is lost sight of.

At this level of mathematics, your child may already be accustomed to applying the distributivity property to numbers and not even thinking about it. Involving variables introduces a new level of sophistication and potential difficulties.

Distributing over a variable and a number One typical form of distributing your child will encounter is:

$$5(x + 3) = 5x + 15$$

Even though this involves exactly the same idea as

$$5(6 + 3) = 30 + 15$$

now that it is more abstract it can be quite difficult for some children. If your child has trouble with this, go back and forth between examples with variables and the same examples with the variables replaced by numbers.

Combining like terms Another typical form of distributing occurs when $3x + 6x$ is combined to make $9x$. Most children see that if you have three x's and you add six more x's, then you will have nine x's—in the same way that if you add three apples to six apples you will have nine apples.

Emphasize that this works because you are adding the same kind of thing together. For example, $300 + 600 = 900$ because three hundreds plus six more hundreds produces nine hundreds. Some children may be tempted to combine terms in an expression like $3x + 6y$—describe this as trying to add apples and oranges, and point out that it is not possible to simplify it.

This idea of *combining like terms* will be important later on in Algebra. You can smooth the way for your child by laying the proper foundation now.

After being introduced to the idea of combining like terms, many children are tempted to simplify the expression

$$3 + 6x$$

as being equal to $9x$. If your child makes this mistake, point out two things.

The first is that if you are adding three ones and six x's, then you are adding apples and oranges and the two terms cannot be combined.

The second is to remind them of PEMDAS, which was discussed in the previous section. Ask your child what the value of $3 + 6 \times 5$ is. If need be, recall that the 6 must be multiplied times the 5 before anything can be added to the 3.

1.8 Two-step equations

LESSON | Learning to solve two-step equations.

Your child needs to be comfortable using reverse operations to solve one-step equations—review Section 1.5: *One-step equations* as needed.

Practice ▶ **Review** The goals listed in Section 1.5: *One-step equations* continue to be the focus for these equations. The reverse operations needed for one-step equations are also needed here. The new skill needed for these equations is recognizing the order that the reverse operations should be done in.

The first step with any equation is to simplify it. Also, if there are variables on both sides of the equation, then they should be placed together on one side of the equation. Both of these skills are covered in later sections, so this section will only look at cleaned up examples.

Peeling an onion Consider these two examples

$$3(x + 2) = 21 \qquad 3x + 2 = 21$$

Seeing the multiplication by 3, and the addition of 2, it seems likely that we will want to divide by 3 and subtract 2 to solve these equations.

Which step is to be done first, and what is the strategy?

I like to compare this to peeling an onion. At the center of the onion is the variable. The layers of the onion are operations that are performed on the variable. These are the layers that will need to be peeled away to get the variable by itself.

Identify the layers of the onion by sticking in a number for the variable, say $x = 5$. Using a number instead of a variable is easier for most children. Ask your child to evaluate the left side of the equation, and write down the steps as it is done.

Using $x = 5$ for the example $3(x + 2)$, this becomes $3(5 + 2)$. The steps are:

1. add 2

2. multiply by 3

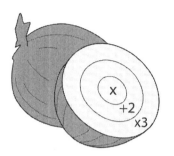

These steps are the layers of your onion. Peel away these layers using reverse operations, starting with the outside layer. To solve this equation

1. divide by 3 (the reverse of multiplying by 3)

2. subtract 2 (the reverse of adding 2)

$$3(x + 2) \div 3 = 21 \div 3$$
$$x + 2 = 7$$
$$x + 2 - 2 = 7 - 2$$
$$x = 5$$

For the example $3x + 2 = 21$, the layers of the onion are:

1. multiply by 3

2. add 2

To solve this equation, peel the onion and do the reverse operations

1. subtract 2

2. divide by 3

$$3x + 2 - 2 = 21 - 2$$
$$3x = 19$$
$$3x \div 3 = 19 \div 3$$
$$x = \frac{19}{3} = 6\frac{2}{3}$$

Two stumbling blocks There are two types of problems that confuse a lot of children. These are problems where you are subtracting or dividing by a variable. For example, $23 - a = 6$ and $36 \div b = 12$.

It is hard to look at these expressions and see them as a series of operations on the variable. The first equation can be transformed to $23 + (-a) = 6$, but working with opposites is beyond the scope of this book. The second can be transformed to $36 \times \frac{1}{b} = 12$. In this form, the layers of the onion are 1) take the reciprocal, and then 2) multiply by 36. This is probably too sophisticated an approach for now.

The easiest way to solve these is to start by reversing the operation that involves the variable. If you add a to both sides of $23 - a = 6$, it becomes $23 = a + 6$, which is easy to solve. Similarly, in $36 \div b = 12$, if you multiply by b this becomes $36 = 12b$.

Create a mystery This is an extension of the mysteries mentioned in Section 1.5: *One-step equations*. For these new mysteries, the card by each doll will have two or more actions that were performed since the theft. A card might read: "After the theft I took 5 steps back, turned right 90 degrees, and then took 8 steps forward." Your child will need to undo or reverse the actions in reverse sequence to figure out which doll was the one that was at the place where the theft happened.

Create problems This is an extension of the problem creation technique mentioned in Section 1.5: *One-step equations*. For these problems, start with something more complicated such as $4x - 3$. As before, decide on a solution, say 15, and substitute it in for x. Next, calculate $4x - 3 = 4 \times 15 - 3 = 57$. This produces the problem $4x - 3 = 57$, which has $x = 15$ as its solution.

Multi-step equations This section has only talked about solving two-step equations. There is not much additional difficulty in going on to equations with more steps. Peeling an onion with three or more layers is not much harder than peeling one with two layers. The main problem is that the mathematical expressions get pretty complicated for children at this level.

1.9 Simplifying equations

LESSON | Learning to clean up and simplify equations.

Practice ▷   At this stage of mathematics the equations will not be all that messy. Even still, there is plenty of opportunity for word problems to generate something that might look like

$$x + 3(x + 7) + (2x + 5) = 50$$

For these problems, the task is to clean up the left side of the equation so that all of the variables are collapsed into one term, and the numbers are collapsed into a second term.

For this particular problem, in order to combine the x's together you must start by distributing.

$$x + 3x + 21 + 2x + 5 = 50$$

Next, rearrange terms to put the x's together and the numbers together.

$$(x + 3x + 2x) + (21 + 5) = 50$$
$$6x + 26 = 50$$

Once the clean up has been done, then the equation is ready to be solved using the tools for that type of equation. In this case, that means using the methods in Section 1.8: *Two-step equations*.

$$6x = 50 - 26 = 24$$
$$x = 24 \div 6 = 4$$

1.10 Variables on both sides

LESSON | Learning to solve equations with variables on both sides.

    These equations involve a single variable that appears on both sides of the equation. Equations of this type are a significant step up in sophistication for your child. As such, if your child has trouble with them you may want to wait a year before trying them again.

The central strategy for these equations is: get all of the variables on one side of the equation. This usually involves subtracting off the variable expression from the side where it is not wanted. Cleaning up the equation is done along the way, as needed.

Take $x + 25 + x - 12 = x + 34$, for example. Start by simplifying this equation to

$$2x + 13 = x + 34$$

Next, get all of the x's on one side of the equation. For this equation, this can either be done by subtracting $2x$ from both sides of the equation (to remove it from the left side), or by subtracting x from both sides of the equation (to remove it from the right side). In theory either one is fine, but to avoid creating negative numbers pick the smaller number of x's. Subtracting x from both sides gives

$$2x + 13 - x = x + 34 - x$$

This needs to be cleaned up, which makes it $x + 13 = 34$.

As another example, consider $5x = 8x - 12$. Avoid negative numbers by subtracting $5x$ from both sides. The equation becomes $0 = 3x - 12$, which is solved as a two-step equation.

1.11   Substitution

LESSON	Learning to use substitution to solve equations with more than one variable.

Practice⟫   In general, handling equations with more than one variable is beyond the scope of this book. However, there is one class of equations that is easier to solve, and shows up frequently in word problems.

Sample problem Al and Bill went shopping and spent 53 dollars. Bill spent 5 dollars more than Al. How much did each spend?

The equations from this story are:

$$53 = Al + Bill$$

$$Bill = Al + 5$$

The method to use to solve these equations is called *substitution*.

> **RULE**   The principle of substitution says that equality is maintained if a quantity in an equation is replaced by something equal to it.

Children use substitution all the time without thinking about it. When $x = 12 + 27$ gets simplified to $x = 39$, they are substituting 39 for the equal quantity $12 + 27$.

To solve the equations in the example above, create an equation that involves only one variable. Do this by substituting the second equation's expression for Bill into the first equation. That equation then becomes easy to solve for Al.

$$53 = Al + Bill = Al + (Al + 5)$$

Solve this last equation to find that Al spent 24 dollars. Then use the formula for Bill in the original second equation to find that value.

$$Bill = Al + 5 = 24 + 5 = 29$$

Key strategy The key strategy in these problems is finding an equation you can use to get rid of one of the variables. Keep repeating that process until there is a single variable remaining.

In the previous problem, the second equation

$$Bill = Al + 5$$

serves that role. We can substitute that equation into any other equation that involves *Bill* to get rid of *Bill* wherever it may occur.

Here is another example:

$$x + 3 = 2y - 8$$
$$x + 12 = 5y - 20$$

Either equation can be used, but let's use the first one. Solve for x in the first equation by subtracting 3 from both sides. This produces the equation:

$$x = 2y - 11$$

This can now be substituted in for x in the second equation:

$$(2y - 11) + 12 = 5y - 20$$

Solve this by first simplifying, and then putting the y's on the right side and the numbers on the left side.

$$2y + 1 = 5y - 20$$
$$1 + 20 = 5y - 2y$$
$$21 = 3y$$

Put the solution $y = 7$ back into the substitution equation to finish the solution:

$$x = 2y - 11 = (2 \times 7) - 11 = 3$$

Notice that the substitution equations alway give you a simple way, at the end of the problem, to calculate the value of the substitution variables.

Substituting in your head Children are often given word problems that involve substitution, but they are asked to do some mental gymnastics in order to make the problem use only one variable.

Consider the word problem given in Section 2.5: *Coin problems* in the *Word Problems* Chapter.

> Bill has three times as many nickels as dimes. The total value of the coins is $3. How many coins of each kind does he have?

One way to do this problem is to let D be the number of dimes, and do everything in terms of D. The value of the dimes is $10D$ cents. Since there are three times as many nickels as dimes, the value of the nickels is $5(3D)$ cents. The total value of the coins is 300 cents, which leads to the equation

$$300 = \text{<dime value>} + \text{<nickel value>} = 10D + 15D = 25D$$

The advantage of this method is that it only involves one variable. However, it is difficult in that it requires remembering that there are three times as many nickels as dimes. The child is doing a substitution; it is just occurring in the child's head rather than on paper.

A far simpler approach is to create equations that come directly from the story, without using any mental gymnastics. That is the solution to this problem provided in Section 2.5: *Coin problems*. This way of doing the problem is more natural for most children and leads to fewer mistakes.

1.12   Solving proportions

Learning to solve equations that are proportions.

RELATED

Equations involving proportions often occur in similar figure geometry problems (Section 6.7: *Similar and congruent shapes*) and in
word problems involving rates (Section 2.8: *Rate problems*).

Practice ▶ **Equivalent fractions** The easiest proportion problems are those that
can be solved using the idea of *equivalent fractions*—fractions are
said to be *equivalent* if they have the same value, such as:

$$\frac{1}{2} = \frac{2}{4} = \frac{3}{6} = \frac{23}{46}$$

Recall from working with fractions that the only way to create
a new fraction equivalent to a given fraction is to multiply or
divide the top and bottom of the the fraction by the same thing.
Use equivalent fractions to solve the next two problems.

$$\frac{2}{7} = \frac{x}{28} \qquad\qquad \frac{12}{44} = \frac{3}{y}$$

For the first equation, the denominator, 7, is multiplied by 4 to
get 28. To get an equivalent fraction, the numerator, 2, must also
be multiplied by 4, which produces: $x = 2 \times 4 = 8$.

In the second equation, the numerator, 12, is divided by 4 to get
3. To get an equivalent fraction, the denominator, 44, must also
be divided by 4, which produces: $y = 44 \div 4 = 11$.

Sometimes a proportion problem can be turned into one of these
easier problems by reducing first. At first glance the problem

$$\frac{6}{21} = \frac{x}{28}$$

looks as though you cannot use the equivalent fraction method
to solve it. However, if you notice that $\frac{6}{21}$ can be reduced to $\frac{2}{7}$,
then the problem turns into the first of the two problems listed
above, and it becomes easy to solve.

More complex proportions The harder proportion problems are of two kinds—one with the variable in the numerator, the other with it in the denominator. Some examples are:

$$\frac{3}{7} = \frac{x}{20} \qquad\qquad \frac{3}{5} = \frac{8}{x}$$

The general approach for these problems is to start by clearing the denominators by cross-multiplying—that is, multiplying the equation by each of the denominators. This clears the denominators and works very well in all cases.

$$\frac{3}{7} = \frac{x}{20} \qquad\qquad \frac{3}{5} = \frac{8}{x}$$
$$3 \times 20 = 7x \qquad\qquad 3x = 8 \times 5$$
$$60 = 7x \qquad\qquad 3x = 40$$
$$60 \div 7 = x \qquad\qquad x = 40 \div 3$$
$$8\frac{4}{7} = x \qquad\qquad x = 13\frac{1}{3}$$

While this method always works, and is good for general use, it is silly to use it for problems similar to the first problem—proportion problems where the variable is in the numerator. If you use cross-multiplying for this problem, then you will multiply by 7 in the first step, and divide by it in the next step. These are easier to treat as one-step equations—simply undo the division by 20 in a single step:

$$\frac{3}{7} = \frac{x}{20}$$
$$\frac{3}{7} \times 20 = x$$
$$8\frac{4}{7} = x$$

1.13 Inequalities and the number line

Learning about inequalities and displaying them on a number line.

 Equations compare two equal quantities. Inequalities compare two quantities, but the quantities need not be equal. We see inequalities all the time in our day-to-day lives. For example, "You must be 18 or older to vote."

Number lines are good tools for visualizing inequality relationships. Always draw your number lines with the numbers increasing to the right. This will allow your child to visually associate larger numbers with going to the right on the line.

For example, compare 2 and 5 by putting them on a number line and seeing that 5 is three more than 2.

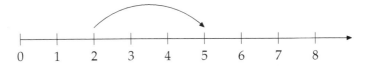

The relationship between 2 and 5 can be described in many ways using the various types of inequalities. 2 is not equal to 5, so $2 \neq 5$. 2 is less than 5, so $2 < 5$. 2 is less than or equal to 5, so $2 \leq 5$. 5 is greater than 2, so $5 > 2$. 5 is greater than or equal to 2, so $5 \geq 2$.

If your child has trouble remembering which way to draw the inequality sign, tell your child that the wider part of the sign goes with the larger number. Some children like to think of the inequality sign as a hungry alligator that is trying to eat the larger number.

When inequalities involve a range of values, darken in all of the values that are valid. Use an arrow at the end of a range to indicate that the range goes on forever.

For example, graph $x \geq 2$ by starting with a dark ball at 2, and then a dark line going to the right, with an arrow at the end.

To exclude a particular value, put a hollow ball around it. Graph $x \neq 3$ by putting a hollow ball at 3, and dark lines going to the left and to the right.

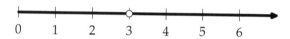

For some problems, it is not appropriate to darken in all of the numbers. For the phrase, "there were at least 3 people at the party," only whole number values are appropriate.

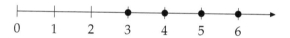

Solving inequalities Everything your child learned about solving equations will work for inequalities. The only difference occurs when multiplying or dividing an inequality by a negative number. Since negative numbers are not covered in this book, I will not discuss that situation any further here.

Here is an example from an earlier section on solving equations to illustrate that the inequality sign does not change any of the solution steps.

$$
\begin{array}{r}
y + 127 < 812 \\
-127 \quad -127 \\
\hline
y < 685
\end{array}
$$

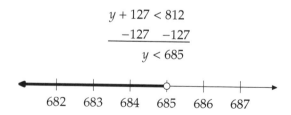

CHAPTER **2**

_____ **Word Problems**

You are asking your child a math word problem every time you ask a question about the world that involves a bit of mathematics. Your child is learning the words, phrases, and ideas of mathematics. This is an important skill, and it is one that will take time and much practice to master.

This chapter provides a systematic way for your child to approach word problems. Following this approach will make elementary word problems straightforward to do. The problems considered in this chapter are kept at an introductory level so that the basic techniques may be practiced.

When selecting problems to practice on, choose word problems at a level that involve equations your child already knows how to solve. Doing this will help your child develop confidence in a set of skills that will form a good foundation for attacking word problems.

This chapter starts off with a section on the most basic word problems. That section is followed by one on how to translate English phrases and sentences into mathematical expressions and equations.

The emphasis in both sections is on having your child become used to working with spoken phrases and turning them into mathematics. Isolating this translation skill makes it easier to see just how mechanical the mathematical translation of English phrases can be.

The games in Section 1.1: *I'm thinking of a number* and Section 1.2: *The bag game* are an excellent source of elementary word problems. These engaging puzzles involve basic math phrases that must be turned into mental equations.

The chapter then presents a five-step method for handling word problems. Practicing these steps on easier problems will develop good habits that will serve your child well when encountering more complex word problems in the years to come.

The chapter follows that with several sections for practicing particular kinds of introductory-level word problems. It presents examples involving ages, coins, whole numbers, distance, speed, and rates. This provides a chance to learn the phrasing used for these different kinds of problems, as well as giving lots of practice. These are typical types of problems your child may see, but they are only meant as examples. If you find some other types of word problems that your child particularly enjoys, do not limit yourself to the kinds given here.

The chapter ends by looking at more advanced ideas involved in word problems. One section gives an introduction to problem solving strategies that are useful when the five-step method is not enough. This is a wonderful group of strategies that your child can develop and grow with over a lifetime. Most of these strategies will prove useful in non-mathematical problem solving as well. The final section studies how to recognize and work with problems which have no solution.

2.1 Beginning word problems

LESSON | Learning how to solve very early word problems.

 Problem progression Working with word problems involves learning how to answer a mathematical question posed in words. A couple of fundamental skills are: 1) learning to take mathematical phrases and recognize the mathematics that they refer to, and 2) learning to solve the associated mathematics. The next section, Section 2.2: *Translating phrases into math*, will look in detail at many of the forms mathematical phrases can take.

At this point, you should select problems that do not involve using any variables or that need to have anything written down. As soon as you need to write things down, you have advanced to the kinds of problems described in Section 2.3: *Five steps*.

The following describes the starting progression of word problems for your child.

Direct calculations The earliest form of word problem is the kind where you ask your child to directly calculate an answer. For example: "What is the sum of 3 and 6?"

You may not even think of this kind of problem as a word problem. However, your child is learning to recognize mathematical phrases and perform the associated arithmetic. As you will discover in the next section, there are a great many short phrases your child will need to learn. We have lots of ways of asking the same thing, and your child will need time to learn them.

Consider all of these ways to ask how much $8 - 3$ is: What is 8 subtract 3? What is 3 less than 8? What is the difference of 8 and 3? What is 8 decreased by 3?

You can add variety and fun to these problems by using items rather than simple numbers. For example: "If two friends are coming to your party and then you invite 3 more, how many friends will be coming to your party?" or "If you have 15 scoops of ice cream and you make ice cream cones with 3 scoops each, how many cones can you make?"

Everyday questions Take advantage of everyday situations to let your child practice with word problems, and use these opportunities to let your child see that math is involved in everyday life.

Some examples of such questions are: "Which of these two lines (at a store) is the shorter one?", "We each like to eat 2 cookies for dessert. How many will we need to buy for the four of us?", and "We can buy one for four dollars or two for seven dollars—which one should we do?"

Missing numbers Once your child gets very good at the direct calculation problems, start asking problems that are missing a number. For example, "If the sum of 3 and a number is 8, what is the number?"

More complicated phrases Bit by bit, as your child gets good at one level of problems, keep putting new ideas into your problems. For example, after your child gets used to solving single-step word problems, try some that are a bit more complicated, such as "If three less than a number is half of 20, what is the number?" You can increase the level of complexity in these problems in the same way that you would create more complicated equations for your child to solve.

For some additional ideas along these lines, look in Chapter 10: *Learning Games and Activities* at the games mentioned in Section 10.2: *I'm thinking of a number* and Section 10.2: *The bag game.* There are lots of problem formats listed there for mathematical word puzzles.

2.2 Translating phrases into math

LESSON │ Translating English phrases into mathematical expressions.

Practice ➤ **Short phrases** There are a number of standard short phrases that translate directly into mathematical expressions.

$2 + x$

the sum of 2 and x	x is increased by 2
2 more than x	2 years from now
2 is added to x	the total of 2 and x
2 and x combined	2 plus x

$x - 2$

difference between x and 2	x is decreased by 2
2 less than x	x minus 2
2 years ago	2 is subtracted from x
x is reduced by 2	2 fewer girls than boys
2 fewer than x	

$2x$

the product of 2 and x	2 times x
2 times as many	2 of x
x increased by a factor of 2	2 multiplied by x
do a rate for 2 time periods	twice x

$x \div 2$

x decreased by a factor of 2	the ratio of x and 2
2 people paid a total of x	quotient of x and 2
x divided into 2 equal groups	x divided by 2

Rates

100 dollars per day	100 dollars a day

$x = 2$

x is the same as 2	x is 2
x equals 2	x yields 2
x becomes 2	x amounts to 2

x

the quantity of x	the total of x

Comparisons Most of the phrases for comparisons use the same words as the name for the comparison. In addition to those, "fewer" is used for "<", "at most" is used for "≤," "more" is used for ">," and "at least" is used for "≥."

Confusions Some of the phrases are easy to get backwards. For example, the phrase "there are twice as many x as y" should be translated as "$x = 2y$," but it is tempting to translate it the other way around. Similarly, "2 less than x" means $x - 2$, not $2 - x$.

A couple of phrases I do not like are "the difference of a and b" and "the difference between a and b." The preferred translation of these is "$a-b$," but I do not agree. Since the difference is just the distance between the two numbers, the phrase "the difference between 2 and 5" should be the same as "the difference between 5 and 2." However, that is not what you will find in most books and classrooms.

Combination phrases Short phrases can be combined into more complicated phrases. The challenge in these phrases is usually in deciding how to group the words.

For example, "five more than 3 times a number" means

five more than (3 times a number)

not

(five more than 3) times a number

This grouping will not be obvious to your child, and it will take practice to develop a sense of how the compound phrases work.

Sentences Using words for equality or comparison, phrases can be put together to create sentences.

Five more than	twice a number	is	3 times the number.
$5+$	$2 \times N$	$=$	$3 \times N$

Complicated mathematical descriptions and concepts can go beyond anything that can be translated easily. For now, stick with simpler word problems where the sentences translate almost word by word into mathematical expressions and equations.

2.3 Five steps

 Learning the five steps for solving word problems.

 Only give word problems to your child that correspond to the level of equations that have been mastered in Chapter 1: *Equations and Inequalities*.

 Practice effective methods I often see children approach word problems by staring and thinking. They write nothing down, and wait for a magical "aha" moment when they see the answer. This works for the simplest word problems, and this success encourages them to keep doing it. They then get stuck on harder problems. Children need a method that will carry them through word problems that are more complicated than they are able to do in their heads.

The five steps Here are five steps that organize an attack for word problems. To keep the steps from seeming overly theoretical, they will be applied to the following simple problem.

Sample Problem: 17 more than a number is 83. What is the number?

1. **Read** Read over the problem and get a general idea of what is going on. Pay special attention to the requested answer.

   The sample problem talks about a number, and asks what its value is.

2. **Name** Make up names to represent quantities that need to be worked with, especially items involved in the answer. Choose variable names that are easily associated with their quantities.

   Let N stand for the number in the problem.

3. **Translate** Translate the English sentences into math. It is very important that your child not try to solve anything during this step. For these easier, beginning problems, you can usually translate them one sentence at a time.

   The sentence in this problem translates to: $17 + N = 83$.

4. Solve Solve the math produced in the last step. If the translation is complete, you should be able to solve the mathematics without referring back to the original words.

Solve the equation from the last step: $N = 83 - 17 = 66$.

5. Check Translate your solution back into the English of the problem. Make sure the solution makes sense in the context of the problem. If the solution makes no sense, a mistake may have been made or it may be that the problem has no solution.

The number is 66, and this works fine in the problem.

Inequalities Mix in occasional word problems that ask for answers that are inequalities. For example, the last word problem could be changed to: 17 more than a number is at least 83. How big is the number?

Translating this to math produces: $17 + N \geq 83$. Solving this gives $N \geq 66$. So, the answer is that the number is at least 66.

Problems with no solution Many reasonable sounding word problems have no solution.

The answers to problems that involve items that cannot be broken into fractional parts must be whole numbers. Similarly, problems with lengths and areas need to have answers with positive amounts.

Have your child make a habit of checking that answers make sense in terms of the items being discussed.

This topic is explored more fully in Section 2.11: *Problems without solutions*.

2.4   Age problems

  Practice solving word problems involving ages.

Practice ▶ **Follow the word problem steps** Sample problem: Ann is 15 years old. Ann's uncle is 3 times as old as she is. How old is her uncle?

Follow the five word problem steps.

1. The problem is talking about two ages, and asks for the uncle's age.
2. Let A and U be the ages of Ann and her uncle.
3. Translate the sentences as: $A = 15$ and $U = 3A$.
4. Since A is 15, substitute this into the second equation to give $U = 3 \times 15 = 45$.
5. Ann's uncle is 45 years old, which is a reasonable answer.

You can choose not to use the variable A, and simply remember that Ann is 15 when translating the second sentence for step 3.

Ages in the future or past The tricky part in these problems is changing the representation of the ages when talking about times in the future or the past. If x represents someone's age today, then $x-4$ is that person's age four years ago and $x+12$ is that person's age 12 years from now.

Sample problem: In 21 years Fred will be four times as old as he is now. How old is Fred now?

Follow the five word problem steps.

1. The problem is talking about Fred's age at various times and asks for his age now.
2. Let F be Fred's age now.
3. Translate the first sentence as: $F + 21 = 4F$.
4. Solve this equation by first subtracting F from both sides and then dividing by 3—this gives $21 = 3F$ and then $7 = F$.
5. Fred is 7 years old, which is a reasonable answer.

2.5 Coin problems

 | Practice solving word problems involving coins.

Practice▷   These problems should be worked in terms of cents, even if the amounts are given in dollars. The variables will be the number of each coin involved in the problem. For example, if nickels are involved, then N might be used to represent the number of nickels, and $5N$ would be the value of the nickels in cents.

Sample problem 1 Mr. Martin needs to put $2.00 in quarters in a parking meter. How many quarters does he need?

Going through the five steps, let q stand for the number of quarters. Instead of using 2 dollars, use 200¢. Translating the first sentence, this becomes $25¢ \times q = 200¢$. Solving for q produces $q = 200¢ \div 25¢ = 8$. Mr. Martin will need 8 quarters.

Sample problem 2 Bill has three times as many nickels as dimes. The total value of the coins is $3. How many coins of each kind does he have?

Going through the five steps, the problem is talking about counts of dimes and nickels, so let D be the number of dimes and N be the number of nickels. Translating the first two sentences into equations gives:

$$N = 3D \qquad 5N + 10D = 300$$

Substituting $N = 3D$ into the second equation makes it

$$5(3D) + 10D = 300$$

This simplifies to $25D = 300$, whose solution is $D = 12$.

If $D = 12$, then $N = 3D = 3 \times 12 = 36$.

So, Bill has 36 nickels and 12 dimes.

2.6 Consecutive number problems

LESSON | Practice solving word problems consecutive numbers.

Practice ▶ **Consecutive whole numbers** Numbers are *consecutive* if they are in a row, each following right after the other. For example, three consecutive whole numbers would be 5, 6, and 7.

Sample problem: The sum of three consecutive numbers is 36, what are the numbers?

Rather than naming all three of the numbers, which would create three variables, name only the first number and write the other numbers in terms of it. If the first number is called x, then the next number is $x + 1$, and the third number will be $x + 2$.

Using this, the phrase "sum of three consecutive numbers is 36" translates to

$$x + (x + 1) + (x + 2) = 36$$

This simplifies to $3x + 3 = 36$, whose solution is $x = 11$. So, the numbers are 11, 12, and 13.

Consecutive even or odd numbers The term consecutive also may be applied to even or odd numbers. Three consecutive even numbers would be 12, 14, and 16, and three consecutive odd numbers would be 95, 97, and 99.

These problems can usually be treated the same as the consecutive whole number problems, only now the gap between the numbers is 2, instead of 1. If x is the smallest of the numbers, then $x + 2$ will be the next one.

Sample problem: The sum of four consecutive odd numbers is 81 more than the smallest number, what are the numbers?

Use a for the smallest of the odd numbers. This gives:

$$a + (a + 2) + (a + 4) + (a + 6) = a + 81$$

This simplifies to $4a + 12 = a + 81$, whose solution is $a = 23$. So, the four numbers are 23, 25, 27, and 29.

2.7 Distance and speed problems

LESSON | Practice solving word problems involving distance and speed.

Practice ▷ **Basic relationships** Distance and speed problems are often used as an introduction to rate problems. The key relationships are:

$$\text{speed} = \frac{\text{distance}}{\text{time}} \qquad \text{time} = \frac{\text{distance}}{\text{speed}} \qquad \text{speed} \times \text{time} = \text{distance}$$

Part of the difficulty of these problems is moving freely among these three relationships.

Sample problem: A family travels 90 miles to the grandparents' house. If the trip takes them $2\frac{1}{2}$ hours, what was their average speed?

Their speed is

$$\frac{90 \text{ miles}}{2\frac{1}{2} \text{ hours}} = \frac{90}{\frac{5}{2}} \times \frac{\text{miles}}{\text{hours}} = \left(90 \times \frac{2}{5}\right) \text{ mph} = 36 \text{ mph}$$

Combined speeds Many of these problems involve two things traveling toward or away from each other. For these problems, the total speed is the sum of their speeds.

Sample problem: Two planes fly toward each other, one at 300 mph and the other at 350 mph. If they start 2,600 miles apart, how long will it take them to pass each other?

300 mph   2,600 miles   350 mph

They are flying toward each other with a combined speed of 650 mph. It will take them

$$\frac{2,600 \text{ miles}}{650 \text{ mph}} = \frac{2,600}{650} \text{ hours} = 4 \text{ hours}$$

2.8 Rate problems

LESSON Learning to solve word problems that involve rates.

RELATED

This section continues the practice begun in the previous section on distance and speed problems. In that section the rate involved was speed, which was the distance traveled over an interval of time. The ideas used in these two sections are really the same. However, speed is more familiar to most children than other rates that occur, so it is worth spending time on that by itself. These sections are also related to the material in Section 7.7: *Rates* in the *Measurements* Chapter.

Practice▶ **Introduction to rates** Advanced rate problems can be quite complicated. The emphasis in this section is on introducing how to work with rates, and practicing word problems.

Sample problem: There is a pipe that leaks water at a rate of 3 gallons a minute. How long will it be before it fills up a protective tank that holds 100 gallons?

Just as for distance, time, and speed, for this problem there are three important relationships.

$$\text{rate} = \frac{\text{volume}}{\text{time}} \qquad \text{time} = \frac{\text{volume}}{\text{rate}} \qquad \text{rate} \times \text{time} = \text{volume}$$

The time to fill up the tank will be

$$\frac{100 \text{ gallons}}{3 \text{ gallons per minute}} = \frac{100}{3} \text{ minutes} = 33\frac{1}{3} \text{ minutes}$$

Consistent units Have your child be on the lookout to convert units to keep the various descriptions consistent. Consider the following problem:

Gasoline costs \$3 a gallon. Joe wants to buy a quart of gasoline for his motor scooter. How much will it cost him?

This problem talks about dollars, gallons, and quarts. These units will need to be consistent before they can be used together. The common units can be chosen however you like, though some choices lead to easier conversions than others.

For this problem, convert the money to cents, and the volumes to gallons. So, gasoline costs 300¢ a gallon, and Joe wants to buy $\frac{1}{4}$ gallon.

The rate relationships for this problem are:

$$\text{rate} = \frac{\text{money}}{\text{volume}} \quad \text{volume} = \frac{\text{money}}{\text{rate}} \quad \text{rate} \times \text{volume} = \text{money}$$

Using this, the $\frac{1}{4}$ gallon will cost

$$\left(300\ \frac{\text{cents}}{\text{gallon}}\right) \times \left(\frac{1}{4}\ \text{gallon}\right) = \frac{300}{4}\ \text{cents} = 75¢$$

So, Joe will need 75¢ to buy the quart of gasoline.

2.9 Bicycle-tricycle problems

LESSON | Solving word problems with two items with a similar component.

 This is a popular class of problems that is quite easy to solve once you are familiar with it. These problems involve two types of things which have a characteristic that differs slightly between the two. For bicycles and tricycles, the characteristic is the number of wheels.

Traditional solution A typical problem of this type is: There is a total of 56 bicycles and tricycles. All combined, they have 130 wheels. How many bicycles are there?

Following the five-step method leads to solving the equations:

$$b + t = 56 \qquad 2b + 3t = 130$$

This can be solved by solving for one of the variables and using substitution. However, there is a much easier way to do this problem!

Simpler solution Here is a simpler way to do this problem. There are 56 vehicles, each of which has at least 2 wheels. This gives a total of 112 wheels. The remaining $130 - 112 = 18$ wheels must be contributed by the one extra wheel on each tricycle. So, there are 18 tricycles, and $56 - 18 = 38$ bicycles.

Chickens and cows There are 32 chickens and cows, and there are a total of 90 legs. How many chickens and cows are there?

All of the animals have at least 2 legs, so that provides $32 \times 2 = 64$ legs. The remaining $90 - 64 = 26$ legs must be provided by the cows, two at a time. So, there are $26 \div 2 = 13$ cows, and $32 - 13 = 19$ chickens.

Text books A last example involves two kinds of text books. A total of 42 books are bought for $1,095—each math book costs $25, and each history book costs $28.

As before, the books cost at least $25, so the 42 books cost at least $42 \times \$25 = \$1,050$. The remaining $\$1,095 - \$1,050 = \$45$ must be from the extra $3 the history books cost. So, there are $\$45 \div \$3 = 15$ history books, and $42 - 15 = 27$ math books.

2.10 Problem solving strategies

| LESSON | Learning about problem solving strategies. |

Practice▷   Almost all beginning word problems can be solved using the five-step method, and it is a very useful tool. However, it will not automatically solve every word problem you come across. In particular, the second and third steps of the method, those that involve translating sentences into math and then solving that math, can be difficult to do for certain problems.

This section contains many of my favorite problem solving strategies. There are entire books written on this topic, so this section will only serve as an introduction to the ideas. If you are interested in looking more deeply into this topic, you might, for example, want to look at the book *Creative Problem Solving in School Mathematics* by Dr. George Lenchner.

Be persistent This is the most important of these strategies. Studies have found a strong correlation between persistence in problem solving and mathematical ability.

Most children will give up on a math problem in less than a minute. They will quickly turn to you and ask for help or even the answer. If you give them the answer, you are reinforcing that your child could not do the problem and that it was a good idea to give up.

Help your child learn persistence by aiding the exploration for the answer without giving it away. Guide them through different approaches to the problem. Show them that problem solving can be viewed as a challenge, that a problem is a fun puzzle or mystery to be unraveled and solved. Teach them to be willing to take a break from a problem and then come back to it for a second try.

Find similar problems you know how to do Ask: "Which problem have you seen (and already know how to do) that reminds you of this problem?" If your child, or you, can identify such a problem, then ask if the method for solving the old problem will work for this new problem.

Learn from simpler problems This is one of my favorite strategies, and it is very useful for non-mathematical problems. There are two ways to use this idea.

One approach is to look for simpler problems that are similar to the current problem. I use this strategy a great deal when tutoring students who are confronting a type of problem that is more complex than what they are used to.

For example, suppose you ask what the average speed is if you have traveled 30 miles in three-fourths of an hour. Your child may be put off by seeing a fraction, $\frac{3}{4}$, and feel confused. In this case, ask your child how to do a problem without a fraction— ask what the average speed is if you traveled 30 miles in 2 hours. Change as little as you can about the problem to make it into one that is familiar. If your child knows to solve this new problem by dividing 30 by 2, ask if that same method can be used to solve the earlier problem.

The second approach is to break the original problem into simpler pieces. For example, suppose you are asked to solve the counting problem at the start of Section 4.7: *Independent vs. exclusive*. This involves counting the number of ways of getting from town A to town D. If you separate this problem into counting the number of ways of going from A to B to D, and counting the number of ways of going from A to C to D, then you have broken the original problem into two problems that are much easier to do.

Do examples and look for patterns Sometimes you look at a problem and have no idea how to solve it in a general way. If you can find a way to work with smaller versions of the original problem, you may be able to find patterns in these examples that will lead to the solution of the general problem. This is an important special case of the previous strategy.

For example, what is the sum of the first 20 odd numbers? This is a problem that young children do not have the tools to solve all at once. However, it becomes easy if you are willing to do smaller examples and look for a pattern. The sum of 1 odd number is 1, of 2 odd numbers is $1 + 3 = 4$, of 3 odd numbers is $1 + 3 + 5 = 9$, of 4 odd numbers is 16, and of 5 odd numbers is 25. At this point, your child may notice the pattern—that the sum is the square of the number of odd numbers you have.

This strategy develops a willingness to go in and play around with the original problem, to try things out and see where they lead, and that is a wonderful habit to develop.

Educated guess and check Doing something called *guess and check* sounds like something that someone does when they have no idea what to do. That is not the case. When done well, this is a very powerful strategy that may quickly lead to a solution that would otherwise be hard to reach. The process of experimenting with and revising the guesses will often lead to understanding how to solve the problem. It is a perfect strategy for a young child that does not have very many sophisticated math tools to use.

For example, suppose you are told that Grace spent 462 dollars buying 20 math and history books. The math books cost 21 dollars and the history books cost 28 dollars. We could solve this problem using equations and substitution, but let's use guess and check instead.

You might make an initial guess that she bought 10 of each—that would lead to a total cost of 490 dollars, which is too high. Lower the total cost by making a new guess that involves buying more of the cheaper books. If you guess that she bought 15 math books, that leads to a total cost of 455 dollars, which is just a little too low. Making a small modification leads to the correct answer: she bought 14 math books and 6 history books.

Pictures and diagrams These tools give you ways to organize and display the data from a word problem in a form that greatly improves understanding.

It is almost always a good idea to make a drawing to go with a geometry problem. If you have a problem that involves a tree and the length of its shadow, draw the situation and fill in the information you are given.

Diagrams are also very useful ways to organize data. For example, Venn diagrams are introduced and used to solve a problem in Section 3.2: *Sets and Venn diagrams*.

Charts For some problems, you may be able to create a chart that takes advantage of a general relationship present in the problem. Rate problems often have this property.

Charts are good organizational tools that make it clear which things are known, which things need to be found out, and what the relationships are. Use a chart to solve the following work rate problem. Roy takes 3 hours to mow a large lawn. Bob takes 2 hours to mow the same lawn. If Roy and Bob work together, how long will it take them to mow the lawn?

The important relationship is that rate × time = work. Here is a table that captures this relationship and the given information:

	rate x	time	= work
Roy		3	1
Bob		2	1
Together			

When faced with this chart, it is compelling to start filling in the rates: $\frac{1}{3}$ for Roy and $\frac{1}{2}$ for Bob. After that, the rate for the two working together will be the sum of their rates, so the rate when they work together is $\frac{5}{6}$. Finally, this produces a time of $\frac{6}{5}$, or 1 hour and 12 minutes, for the time it will take them to mow the lawn together.

Make a table of information This is similar to making a chart. If there is a lot of data in a problem, have your child record it in an organized way.

For example, I mentioned earlier in this section doing examples for the sum of the first few odd numbers. In doing that problem, you could have your child make a table with two columns—the first column has the number of odd numbers and the second has their sum.

It is a lot easier to see patterns in an organized chart than in notes scattered around a piece of paper.

Act out the scenario For some children, it can help tremendously if they act out, either in reality or in their heads, the scenario of the problem. If there are a sequence of steps, say buying and selling something, have your child act out the steps to see how the problem will work out.

Work with others There are two things that are important about working with others. The first is that it teaches your child the value of sharing ideas—that two children may each have something valuable to offer the other. It is important for your child to learn that doing mathematics need not be an isolating pursuit. The second is that it takes practice to develop the social skills for being able to effectively work with others.

Work backwards Some problems are easier to work backwards than they are forwards.

For example, take the simple problem of finding the number that when you double it and add 5 it equals 23. You could do this by using guess and check and working forwards. However, it is easier to start at the end, 23, and work backwards—take 5 away from 23 to get 18, and then take half of 18 to get 9.

Partial solutions are valuable Most people who fail to solve a problem feel that, since they didn't solve the problem, their work on the problem must be worthless. Encourage your child to value partial solutions. Do this by starting with what has been done so far and demonstrating how it can be extended to a solution of the problem. Eventually, over many years, your child will learn to come back to partial solutions and push through the roadblocks to finish the problem—this is persistence at its best.

2.11   Problems without solutions

 Learning about problems with no solutions.

   Whenever your child solves a word problem, there is always the chance that there will be no solution, or that the solution makes no sense in the world of the problem. Almost all of the problems your child sees in school have nice, tidy solutions. At first, it will come as a big surprise that this is not always the case.

There are many possible ways that problems can have difficulties with their answers. Let's explore how this can happen.

Mistakes The first question to ask is "Was a mistake made?" Encourage your child to make a habit of going back over work to make sure that every step was done correctly. Sometimes this is the end of this journey—a mistake was made, and that led to not finding a solution or finding one that made no sense.

However, there are other possibilities.

No mathematical solution There are some equations that your child will not be able to solve. For example:

$$x^2 = {}^-4 \qquad \text{and} \qquad \frac{2y + 1}{y - 1} = 2$$

This happens extremely rarely at this level. For the level of problems your child is working with, if the mathematics has no solution, it will almost always be the case that a mistake has been made.

The solution makes no sense It is one thing to have a mathematically correct solution, it is quite another for that solution to make sense in the world of the problem.

For the types of problems your child is likely to see, here are the most common kinds of problems that may have answers that cannot be used.

Answers that must be positive A geometry problem that asks for the length of a side or the area of a region must have an answer that is positive. Consider the following problem:

> A rectangular pen is to be built using 400 feet of fencing. How wide should it be if the length needs to be 210 feet more than the width?

The mathematical solution to this is that the width is ⁻5 feet and the length is 205 feet. This is clearly an unusable answer in the real world.

There are a great many problems that involve the measurement of positive quantities of things such as duration, length, area, or a substance (such as cups of flour). For these kinds of problems, the answers must be thrown out if they are not positive.

Answers that must be whole numbers A word problem that involves an item that only comes in whole units cannot have a fractional answer. Sometimes the answer can be adjusted to a real-world answer and sometimes the answer simply makes no sense.

Here are two problems that have answers that are easy to adjust.

> Bonnie is making sundaes with 3 scoops of ice cream in each one. If Bonnie has 14 scoops of ice cream, how many sundaes can she make?

The strict mathematical answer is $14 \div 3 = 4\frac{2}{3}$. However, it's not possible to make $\frac{2}{3}$ of a sundae. In this case, you adjust the mathematical answer by rounding down and saying that only 4 sundaes can be made.

> Bonnie and her friends are going to the movies. How many cars will be needed if there are 14 children and each car can carry 3 children?

Again, the mathematic answer is $4\frac{2}{3}$ cars, but this makes no sense. This time, since there cannot be $\frac{2}{3}$ of a car, the adjustment is to round the answer up to say that 5 cars are needed.

There are many problems for which fractional answers cannot be adjusted.

Danny has a total of 13 coins consisting of pennies and nickels. If the value of his coins is 23 cents, how many nickels does he have?

The mathematical solution is $2\frac{1}{2}$ nickels and $10\frac{1}{2}$ pennies. However, it is impossible to have a fraction of a coin, so this problem does not have an answer that makes sense in the real world.

Misc. unusual answers There are some problems whose mathematical answers are simply not consistent with common sense. For example:

The sum of the ages of Becky and her grandfather is 66. If Becky is half the age of her grandfather, how old is Becky?

The solution to this is that Becky is 22 and her grandfather is 44. However, that solution is not consistent with common sense.

CHAPTER **3**

_____ **Reasoning**

This chapter covers four broad areas of reasoning:

- Sorting and Classifying

- Working with Collections as Sets

- Patterns and Relationships

- Logic

Identifying characteristics of objects, and of groups of objects, is a critical skill children need to understand the world around them. Children use this skill as they come to understand the similarities and differences among animals, people, trees, places, and everything else. Sorting and classifying things into various groups is a good way to practice this. This teaches your child to focus on distinguishing characteristics, and to exclude from consideration other characteristics.

As your child gets older, more of your discussions involving collections of objects can be framed in the language of sets. The section on sets briefly describes the basic terminology, and demonstrates the use of Venn diagrams to organize and calculate with information about overlapping sets.

A basic aspect of mathematics is the discovery of patterns, and learning how to apply them. Initially, the characteristics your child will be considering will be tangible, such as shape and color. As your child's mathematical skills develop, more and more of the characteristics will involve numerical or abstract relationships.

The last part of this chapter covers beginning ideas in logic. This is based on common sense, and is not done in any formal way. An example of this kind of thinking is: "if all other possibilities have been ruled out, the remaining one must be true." These ideas will become more natural and automatic as your child practices them.

There are three software products that are particularly outstanding for practicing patterns and logical reasoning. "Mosaic Magic" by Kinder Magic Software is a wonderful program, particularly good for small children. It works with colored tiles that have to fit in various patterns and relationships. Kids learn to identify and construct the correct tile that will fit a pattern. "Pit Droids" by Lucas Arts Entertainment requires your child to discover patterns and learn ways to make those patterns continue. The "Zoombinis" software games by Broderbund have adventures that involve fun puzzles that are a combination of patterns and logic.

3.1 Sorting and classifying

LESSON Using characteristics to sort and classify objects.

Practice▷ **Simple and concrete** Start simply by considering just one character-istic at a time. Do it with small objects you can place in front of your child. For example, give your child a collection of blocks that have different shapes, sizes, and colors. Ask your child to sort the blocks by shape, or by size, or by color. Point out that the groupings are different depending on which characteristic is being used for sorting.

Everywhere and everything Practice sorting and classifying with all the things in your lives—with toys, with things in the kitchen, with things you see on a walk, with things you see while driving around, with things in the park.

Be alert to using lots of different characteristics, for example:

Shape: round, square, pointy, convex, concave

Texture: smooth, rough, bumpy, ridged, sticky

Size: large, small, tiny, huge, tall, short, long, wide, skinny

Color: red, green, dark, light

Sound: loud, soft, high-pitched, low-pitched

List characteristics One way to practice sorting and classifying is to start with a single object. Make a list with your child of all the characteristics you can think of about that object. Then, for each characteristic on the list, make a list or collection of other things that have that same characteristic.

Complicated characteristics After a great deal of practice, start using characteristics that are more complicated. This can be done in a great many ways. As some examples, sort things by finding things that:

- do not have a certain characteristic

- have both of two characteristics

- have one but not the other of two characteristics

- have all of a list of characteristics

- have any of a list of characteristics

- have at least two of a list of characteristics

- have all of one list of characteristics, but none of another list of characteristics

Sorting laundry Sorting clothes and putting them away is a natural time to talk about sorting and classifying. Have your child put all of one type of clothes, such as socks, in a pile. Talk about why some socks match up and others do not. Have your child put all of one person's clothes in a pile.

Trips to the store Have your child help you find things in the store. Talk about how the items are grouped on the shelves, and what the characteristics are of the item you are searching for.

Making collections Anything your child enjoys collecting provides an opportunity to talk about sorting and classifying. Whether it is stamps, rocks, flowers, or pictures, forming and arranging a collection will give you lots of characteristics to use to talk about how things are similar or different.

Quarto! and Set These are fun games that young children and adults can play. They involve playing pieces or cards that have several characteristics that need to be matched up. Read more about them in Section 10.1: *Logic or patterns* in the *Learning Games and Activities* Chapter.

3.2 Sets and Venn diagrams

 | Learning about sets and Venn diagrams.

    As your child gets used to working with collections of objects, mix in using a little of the vocabulary of sets.

> **MATH WORDS** A *set* is a collection or group of things. The things in the set are called the *elements* or *members* of the set.

One way to write a set is to list the members of the set inside curly braces. For example, $A = \{1, 3, 5, 7\}$ describes A as the collection consisting of four elements, which are the first four odd numbers. When describing a set, the order of the elements is not important.

Venn diagrams A Venn diagram is a drawing showing sets as overlapping circles. The region of overlap of two circles represents the members that are in both of the sets.

These diagrams are useful for getting a quick visual understanding of how the various parts of sets relate to each other. Here is an example of using a Venn diagram to solve a counting problem.

There are 456 students taking Chemistry or Physics. There are 225 students taking Chemistry, and of those 120 are taking Physics. How many students are taking Physics?

A Venn diagram does not solve the problem for you, but it makes it easier to see how to work with the information. Each of the 456 students is represented by one of the parts of the diagram. So, all of the parts of the diagram add up to 456.

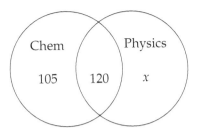

The first observation to make is that if there are 225 students taking Chemistry, and there are 120 students taking both Physics and Chemistry, then there must be $225 - 120 = 105$ students taking Chemistry but not taking Physics. Let x be the number of Physics students not taking Chemistry.

At this point we can fill in every region of the diagram with a number or a variable expression. The parts of the diagram taken together account for all of the 456 students. That leads to the following equation:

$$456 = 105 + 120 + x$$
$$= 225 + x$$

Solving this yields: $x = 456 - 225 = 231$. The number of students taking Physics is $x + 120$, which is $231 + 120 = 351$.

RELATED   This counting method is explored further in Section 4.3: *Counting parts* in the *Probability and Counting* Chapter.

3.3 Patterns

LESSON Discovering and applying patterns.

Practice ➤ **Listen to reasoning** Create sequences long enough that the pattern repeats at least two times. For example:

red red green red red green ____ ____ ____.

If your child comes up with a different answer than you expect, discuss the reasoning behind your child's answer. Your child may have picked up on some different characteristics of the objects than you were thinking of.

Different types For small children, choose things that are easy to interact with. The simplest way to do this is to use blocks or small food items on a table or floor where your child can move them around.

Many other types of patterns can be used:

Body positions arms crossed, arms overhead, arms crossed, arms overhead. Here are some children doing the YMCA pattern.

Walking step step hop hop step step hop hop. This is a fun thing to do when you are walking somewhere.

Sounds with hands, feet, or mouth clap snap clap quiet clap snap clap quiet.

Rhythm patterns Use sounds or movements to produce the rhythms. For example, slow quick quick slow quick quick.

Number patterns As your child grows older, start using patterns involving numbers. For younger children, use simpler patterns with small numbers, such as:

$$1\ 2\ 3\ 4\ 5\ \_\ \_$$
$$6\ 6\ 5\ 5\ 4\ 4\ \_\ \_$$
$$1\ 3\ 5\ 7\ 9\ 11\ \_\ \_$$
$$1\ 2\ 4\ 5\ 7\ 8\ 10\ \_\ \_$$
$$5\ 6\ 4\ 5\ 3\ 4\ \_\ \_$$

For older children, the patterns can involve more complex arithmetic operations. Start with some standard patterns, and then start including some additional changes. As with the earlier patterns, include enough numbers so that the pattern is clear and unambiguous.

$$1\ 4\ 9\ 16\ 25\ 36\ 49\ \_\ \_$$
$$2\ 6\ 12\ 20\ 30\ 42\ 56\ \_\ \_$$
$$1\ 2\ 6\ 24\ 120\ 720\ \_\ \_$$
$$1\ 1\ 2\ 3\ 5\ 8\ 13\ 21\ \_\ \_$$

Take turns Have your child create the pattern for you sometimes. The act of creating a pattern, and checking the other person's answer, causes important insights that are different from discovering another person's pattern.

Nature patterns In addition to the patterns you create for each other, your child will enjoy finding patterns in nature. Your child can investigate the pattern of how leaves grow on trees, or look at the patterns in snowflakes, or describe what happens when an area of dirt gets partially eroded by water. Looking at the patterns of nature is part of the journey down the road to becoming a scientist.

Man-made patterns There are lots of patterns to be found and described in the man-made objects around us.

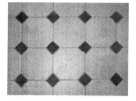 

Tiled floors tend to have lots of interesting patterns. Look for
patterns in the tiling your child did in Section 6.1: *Designs and
patterns*. There are patterns to investigate in the construction of
buildings, in the layout of streets, or in the layout of crops in a
field.

When you drive by crops laid out in a field in a rectangular grid,
talk about the clear diagonals you see in the crops. There are
major diagonals corresponding to moving up 1 and over 1 in the
rows and columns of the crop. There are also other diagonals
you will notice, such as moving up 2 and over 1. See if your
child can discover where the diagonals come from.

3.4 Analogies

Practicing analogies, a special kind of pattern.

 Practice ▷   In analogies, use the relationship between one pair of things to predict what is needed to make the same relationship in another pair of things. For example, "girl is to mother as boy is to ____."

This is very similar to working with patterns. The main difference is that there are only three things given, so it is very easy for you and your child to have different answers.

Suppose you have "2 is to 6 as 4 is to ____." One person might think that 2 was increased by 4 to get 6, so the answer is $4 + 4 = 8$. Another person might think 2 was multiplied by 3 to get 6, and get the answer $4 \times 3 = 12$. One answer is no more correct than the other. Use getting different answers as an opportunity to talk with your child about different ways of looking at a problem.

For young children, it is easiest to start with pictures. For example:

Using pictures makes it easy to change more than one characteristic at once.

As with patterns, as your child gets older transition to doing more of the analogies using numbers.

3.5 Logic

| Introducing beginning ideas in logic.

 Incidental logic Children learn logic incidentally as they do things in the world, and as they discuss "why"s and "how come"s of things with those around them. Casually introduce some of these basic building blocks of logic so that these tools become more available and easier to use.

Among many logical things that your child is learning, there are a few main logical ideas that you can be reinforcing. There is no need to use this terminology with your child; it is introduced here just for this discussion.

Propositions A *proposition* is a statement that has the potential for being true or false. As some examples: "All horses are animals," and "Some animals have four legs."

You can put two propositions together to create a third proposition. For example: "We never get mail on Sundays," and "Today is Sunday," so "We will not get mail today."

Some propositions follow directly from other propositions. The most frequent is called the *contrapositive*. An example of this is: "All horses are animals," so "If something is not an animal, it must not be a horse."

There are some common mistakes made with propositions. The proposition "Some men are mean," does not imply either that "A mean person must be a man," or that "All men are mean."

The last idea to mention here is the idea of *exclusion*. If you know that exactly one thing in a group of things is true, that can lead to some interesting consequences. In particular, if you can find out that all but one of the things in that group are false, then the remaining item must be true.

Puzzle books Most of the practice with logic ideas will be done with day-to-day things. However, there are some very good puzzle books that can give focused practice. For younger children, stay with the easiest of these puzzles.

Critical Thinking Books & Software puts out a series of books called *Mind Benders* that my children enjoyed a great deal. These books contain logical puzzles that use the idea of exclusion to narrow down to a final answer. The books come with gridded charts that are very satisfying to fill in.

Here is an example of this kind of puzzle. Ann, Bonnie, and Celia are married to Al, Bert, and Charlie, though not necessarily in that order. No one is married to someone whose name starts with the same letter. Charlie likes to play tennis with Bonnie's husband. Who is married to whom?

This kind of puzzle is done by making a grid of the possibilities, and then putting X's for combinations that are not possible, and O's for combinations that should go together. Recording the initial clues we have:

	Al	Bert	Charlie
Ann	X		
Bonnie		X	X
Celia			X

Since there are no other possibilities, Charlie must be married to Ann, and Bonnie must be married to Al.

	Al	Bert	Charlie
Ann	X	X	O
Bonnie	O	X	X
Celia	X		X

That in turn forces Celia and Bert to be married.

Sudoku puzzles These are popular puzzles that are 9 by 9 grids—there are smaller, simpler grids available for children. The challenge is to fill in the empty boxes so that each row, column, and 3 by 3 box contains the numbers from 1 to 9 exactly once. A surprising amount of logic is used in solving one of these puzzles. There are many fun variations of these puzzles, such as KenKen or Kakuro.

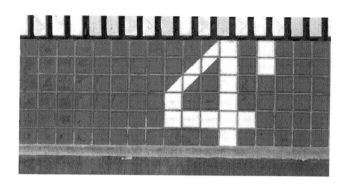

CHAPTER **4**

Probability and Counting

This chapter contains two closely connected topics—probability and counting. These topics are interwoven throughout the chapter.

Games and chance As your child starts playing games of chance, and starts wondering how likely things are to happen, your child will start being involved with probability. Since this exploration will often be connected with games, this is usually a lot of fun.

Introduce your child to probability in simple day-to-day things. If a shirt needs to be taken out of a drawer, ask your child to try it with eyes closed, and talk about the probability of getting the right shirt.

The central theme for calculating probabilities is that the probability of something occurring is the number of ways it can occur successfully divided by the number of ways that anything can occur. For example, if there are 2 dark pairs of socks and 3 light pairs, the probability is $\frac{2}{5}$ of picking a dark pair of socks without looking. Emphasize that this formula is only true when all of the possibilities you are counting are equally likely to happen.

Likely, not guaranteed Impress upon your child that probability is not a guarantee, it is a likelihood. The probability of getting heads is $\frac{1}{2}$, but that does not mean that when you flip a coin 100 times it will be heads 50 times.

The only time an outcome is guaranteed is when the probability is 0 or 1. If the probability is 0, then the outcome cannot occur, and if the probability is 1, the outcome must occur.

Independent events can be counterintuitive Events are said to be *independent* if they do not influence each other in any way. It is difficult for some people to believe that independent events are truly independent.

If you have flipped a coin 5 times and you have seen 5 tails, many adults will say one of two things. Some will say that since heads should occur half of the time, you are overdue to get heads on the next flip. Other adults will say that there is clearly a run of tails going on, so the next flip is much more likely to be tails. Teach your child that the probability is still $\frac{1}{2}$ that it will be heads on the next flip. Independent events, such as coin flips, have no memory—the probability remains the same, no matter what the history is.

With all of the formulas and calculations, it is easy to lose sight of the feeling of the subject. Sometimes, just talk about whether something is more likely or less likely to happen. For example, look at some incoming large, dark clouds and talk about whether it seems likely to rain.

Learn the methods Teach your child the techniques and ideas behind the counting formulas. The formulas do not need to be memorized if the methods behind them are understood.

As discussed in the introduction to this book, your child will benefit from being taught many of these topics through problem solving. Rather than starting a new topic with a rule for how things are done, start with a number of example problems and see if your child can be guided to discovering the rule.

There is a style of thinking for this kind of counting that, once learned, feels natural and is quite powerful. Children enjoy the way the counting ideas fit together, and they enjoy the large numbers that are produced by a little multiplying and a few factorials.

Counting is very important to probability. The counting material in this chapter supports calculations of probability, but it is also interesting in its own right. For years my children have enjoyed being able to calculate the number of glass clinks when a group of people are at my house making a toast.

Some history Risk taking, and its associated thoughts of probability, have been around for thousands of years. The Babylonians had forms of insurance for merchant sea voyages, the Romans had annuities in which a one-time lump-sum payment could be made in exchange for a large number of periodic payments, and of course gambling has been around for all of recorded history. However, all of this risk taking was done by feeling, without any systematic way of calculating the related probabilities.

There are two independent efforts given credit for establishing a more rigorous view of probability. Gerolamo Cardano was an Italian physician, mathematician, and gambler living in the 1500's. He wrote a book on some basic principles of probability in 1525, but it was not published and recognized until 1663. Later, in 1654, there was a gambling question that led to a correspondence between two famous French mathematicians, Blaise Pascal and Pierre de Fermat. From their letters and ideas sprang the foundations for the modern view of probability.

Your child may enjoy investigating and learning about the development of probability since the time of Pascal and Fermat. Enter "probability" and "history" into any internet search engine, and you will find a wealth of sources.

Shameless plug The book *Introduction to Counting & Probability* by David Patrick, published by the Art of Problem Solving, covers the topics of this chapter in much more depth, provides a great many exercise problems, and covers many topics that are natural extensions. The interested child will find this book an excellent way to enjoy more material on this subject.

4.1 Basic probability

 LESSON | Learning the basic ideas of probability.

Practice ▶ **Events** An *event* is a collection of possible outcomes (possibilities).

For example, rolling an odd number with a die is an event. It consists of the three possibilities of rolling a 1, 3, or 5.

Equally likely possibilities The simplest, and most common, form of probability involves possibilities that are equally likely.

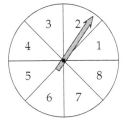 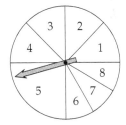

Show your child these pictures of two spinners. With the first spinner, the 8 regions are equal in size, so the spinner is equally likely to land on each one. In the second spinner, the region for the 5 is quite large, so it is far more likely to be chosen.

Definition of probability This next definition of probability only applies when equally likely possibilities are involved. I will use the notation $P(Event)$, or more briefly $P(E)$, to refer to this probability.

 The *probability* of an event, $P(E)$, equals

$$\frac{\text{Number of possibilities in the event}}{\text{Total number of possibilities}}$$

Counting is central to this definition of probability. Because of this, most of this chapter will be spent looking at ways to count things.

Examples When you flip a coin there are two possibilities that are equally likely—heads and tails. There is only one way to get a head, so the probability of getting a head is $\frac{1}{2}$.

As another example, if you roll one die, what is the probability that you will get less than a 3? With a fair die, the six numbers are equally likely. There are two ways to be successful—to roll a 1 or a 2. There are a total of six possibilities. So, the probability is $\frac{2}{6}$, which is $\frac{1}{3}$.

Range of probability values The value of any probability is somewhere from 0 to 1.

If the probability is 0, that means the event is impossible. The probability of rolling a 7 with one die is 0. If the probability is 1, that means that the event is certain to happen. The probability is 1 of rolling a number that is somewhere from 1 to 6.

No guarantees Unless the probability of an event is 0 or 1, there is no guarantee that the event will occur as often as the probability indicates. For example, the probability of getting heads with a flipped fair coin is $\frac{1}{2}$. However, if you flip a coin 2 times, you will often see a total of 0 heads or 2 heads.

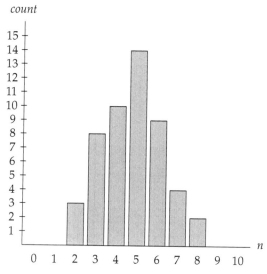

This histogram shows the number of times n heads occurred when I flipped a group of 10 pennies 50 times.

Make graphs of your own experiments Do experiments like this last one with your child. Flip a coin 10 times and record how many heads you see. Do this as many times as your child is interested. You may want to do a frequency graph, covered in Section 5.2: *Tables of data*, to make the results easier to look at. You will probably see that getting 4, 5, and 6 heads is most common, but that other numbers happen as well.

A similar experiment is to keep track of dice rolls. Make a bar graph on some graph paper for the numbers from 2 to 12. Each time your child rolls the dice, darken in one more square in the column above the number for the sum that was rolled. At first the height of the columns will not form much of a pattern. With enough rolls you should see a flowing curve with 7 occurring the most in the middle. Discuss with your child why it took a large number of rolls before it started to look like a nice curve.

Practice while playing games Have your child practice these ideas in any game that involves picking a number at random—whether it uses cards, spinners, or dice. Before some of the turns, have your child calculate the probability of getting the desired numbers, or the probability of avoiding the bad numbers.

RELATED

There are many times when your child will be gathering and displaying data, and those are excellent opportunities to practice the skills in Chapter 5: *Statistics and Graphing*.

4.2 Counting sequences

LESSON | Learning to count sequences.

Practice ▷ **The start of counting** Sophisticated counting starts with learning to count the simple sequence

$$1, 2, 3, \ldots, n$$

This may sound silly, but it is surprisingly important.

Sequences with consecutive numbers The next step is counting the number of terms in a sequence like

$$23, 24, 25, \ldots, 48$$

It is clear that the answer should be something close to $48 - 23$.

Rather than giving your child the answer to this question, make it an exercise in problem solving. There are two important ideas in problem solving that can be practiced with this.

RULE Problem Solving Principles
Two ways to solve a hard problem:
1. Transform it into a problem you know how to do.
2. Solve simpler problems like it, and learn from them.

Using the first principle, transform the sequence to something that starts "1, 2, 3" by subtracting 22 from each of the entries. The sequence becomes

$$1, 2, 3, \ldots, 48 - 22$$

which has $48 - 22 = (48 - 23) + 1$ entries.

Alternatively, use the second principle and find the number of entries in a short sequence such as $23, 24, 25$. Clearly there are 3 entries, which is $(25 - 23) + 1$. After a few more small examples, your child should see that the number of entries is one more than the difference of the first and last entries.

Easy to practice You may see these counting problems as being abstract. However, they are the same as asking how many pages your child read in going from page 23 to page 48 in a book. Asking such questions is an excellent way for your child to practice this skill.

Sequences with consecutive multiples The next type of sequence, that is a bit more complex, is one where the terms are multiples of some number. For example, how many multiples of 7 are there between 40 and 150?

The first multiple of 7 is 42, and the last one is 147. So, how many terms are there in the sequence

$$42, 49, 56, \ldots, 147$$

Turn this into a simpler sequence of the same length by dividing every term in the sequence by 7.

$$6, 7, 8, \ldots, 21$$

The length of this sequence is $(21 - 6) + 1 = 16$.

Arithmetic sequences An arithmetic sequence is one where each term increases by a constant amount. Here is an arithmetic sequence starting at 45, and increasing by 7 up to 150.

$$45, 52, 59, \ldots, 150$$

By subtracting 3 from each term, this sequence can be turned into a sequence of multiples of 7, which was done above.

$$42, 49, 56, \ldots, 147$$

Misc. sequences Look for ways to transform odd sequences into sequences you know how to count. Use the rule that defines the sequence to modify it to something simpler.

For example, consider the problem of counting all of the squares between 200 and 550. The first square bigger than 200 is $221 = 11^2$, and the last square less than 550 is $529 = 23^2$.

Find the length of the sequence

$$11^2, 12^2, 13^2, \ldots, 23^2$$

by associating it with the sequence of the same length which is just the numbers that are being squared

$$11, 12, 13, \ldots, 23$$

4.3 Counting parts

 LESSON | Counting a collection by counting the parts that make it up.

You may want to work through the Venn diagram material in Section 3.2: *Sets and Venn diagrams* when doing this step.

Practice ▷ **Separate collections** If two collections have nothing in common, then the total is the sum of the counts for the two collections. This is a simple idea, but it can be used powerfully. For example, in the next section it is used to count a collection by counting everything that is not in it.

> **RULE** If collections A and B have nothing in common, then the total number of things when A and B are combined is the number of things in A plus the number of things in B.

Look to solve counting problems by breaking them up into separate parts that are easier to count individually.

An example is: "How many two-digit numbers are there whose ones digit is at least three times as big as its tens digit?" Break this into separate cases that depend on the tens digit. There are seven numbers that start with 1 (13, 14, 15, 16, 17, 18, 19), four numbers that start with 2 (26, 27, 28, 29), and one number that starts with 3 (39)—for a total of $7 + 4 + 1 = 12$ numbers.

Overlapping collections Consider two collections, A and B, that may contain some items in common.

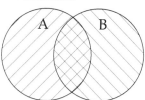

Suppose we want to count the total number of items in A to-gether with B. The Venn diagram demonstrates that if we just add the number of things in A to the number of things in B, we will have counted the items common to A and B twice. So, we need to adjust for this double counting.

> **RULE** The number of items in A combined with B is equal to the number of things in A, plus the number of things in B, minus the number of things they have in common.

Here is an example from around the house. Bob has 12 pairs of socks and his brother has 15 pairs. They share their white pairs, so together they only have 21 pairs of socks. How many pairs of white socks do they have?

$$21 = \text{Bob's} + \text{brother's} - \text{white pairs}$$
$$= 12 + 15 - x$$

Practicing There are quite a few counting situations that have over-lapping characteristics, and those can all use the ideas of this section.

Use situations about your child's friends, clothing, toys, or any other group of things that may be of interest. Make up word problems about a situation that involves some characteristics that may be shared among the items.

For example, you could talk about shirts that are for school and shirts that are used for exercise—if there are 12 shirts all together, 8 of which are school shirts and 6 of which are sports shirts, how many shirts are used for both?

As another example, talk about friends that like different activities. How many of 8 friends like to play soccer if 5 like to read books and 3 enjoy both reading and playing soccer?

4.4 Counting the wrong things

LESSON | Counting a collection by counting what is not in the collection.

Practice ▷   The previous section showed that some situations are most easily counted by breaking them into separate parts that may be counted individually. This section continues with that idea.

     Sometimes it is easier to find out the count you need by counting the wrong things. It may be simpler to count everything, count the things you do not want, and then take the difference of those two to find the count for the things you do want.

everything

right things | wrong things

Example 1 Suppose you are asked how many numbers there are from 1 to 100 that are not squares. The easiest way to do this problem is to count the number of squares (the things not wanted), and subtract that from 100. There are 10 squares in this range, so there are $100 - 10 = 90$ numbers which are not squares.

Example 2 What is the number of ways of getting 1 or more heads when a coin is flipped 4 times? This may be answered by counting the number of ways of getting 1 head, 2 heads, 3 heads, and 4 heads, and then adding those up.

     A far simpler way is to count all possible ways of flipping a coin 4 times (no matter what the result), and then subtract the number of ways of getting 0 heads. In Section 4.6: *Counting independent events*, you will see that there are 16 ways to flip a coin 4 times. Of those 16, there is only one way to get tails for all 4 flips. So, there are $16 - 1 = 15$ ways to get 1 or more heads.

4.5 Combining probabilities

LESSON   Learning rules for how to combine probabilities.

Practice ▶ **Combined events** In Section 4.3: *Counting parts* I described how to count the size of combined collections. Since events are collections of possibilities, the same thing happens for events.

> **RULE** The probability that either A or B occurs equals the probability that A occurs, plus the probability that B occurs, minus the probability that both A and B occur:
>
> $P(A \text{ or } B) = P(A) + P(B) - P(A \text{ and } B)$.

Two events are said to be *disjoint* if the collections of possibilities that make up the events have nothing in common. In the case that A and B are disjoint, then $P(A \text{ and } B) = 0$, and the probability rule simplifies to $P(A \text{ or } B) = P(A) + P(B)$.

As an example, let event A be that a rolled die is odd, and event B be that it is less than 3. There are three possible odd numbers, so $P(A) = \frac{3}{6}$. There are two numbers less than 3, so $P(B) = \frac{2}{6}$. There is one odd number that is less than 3, so $P(A \text{ and } B) = \frac{1}{6}$. Using the rule

$$P(A \text{ or } B) = \frac{3}{6} + \frac{2}{6} - \frac{1}{6} = \frac{4}{6}$$

This is the correct result, since there are four numbers that are either odd or less than 3.

Here is a way to demonstrate how the rule works looking at the overlapping events and their associated probabilities.

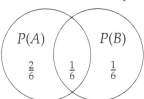

Complement of an event The *complement of an event* is the collection of all possibilities that do not occur in it. For an event, E, I will write its complement as "not E."

Since E and its complement make up all possibilities, then $P(E$ or (not E)) $= 1$. Also, notice that E and its complement are disjoint. Therefore,

$$P(E) + P(\text{not } E) = P(E \text{ or (not } E)) = 1$$

Rewriting this last equation gives:

> **RULE** The probability of E not happening is equal to 1 minus the probability of E happening:
>
> $P(\text{not } E) = 1 - P(E)$.

For example, let E be the event that a roll of a die is less than 3. There are two ways to be less than 3, so $P(E) = \frac{2}{6}$. Consequently

$$P(\text{not } E) = 1 - \frac{2}{6} = \frac{4}{6}$$

This is correct, since there are four ways for the roll to be not less than 3.

everything

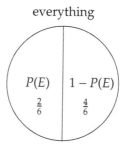

Practicing A good source of these problems is to use the counting problems you created for Section 4.3: *Counting parts* and Section 4.4: *Counting the wrong things*.

4.6   Counting independent events

LESSON   Learning how to count independent events.

Practice ▸   **One from column A, B, and C**   Choices are *independent* if they do not effect each other.

> **RULE**   For a sequence of independent choices, the total count of possibilities is the product of the individual counts.

Drawing a tree of possibilities is a great way to show how all of the combinations multiply together.

Suppose you are creating three letter "words" with these letters: the first letter is one of b, r, or t, the second letter is either a or e, and the last letter is either d or t. Each choice has no effect on the other choices. So, there are $3 \times 2 \times 2$ possible "words."

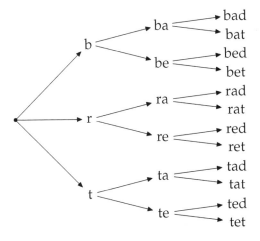

After making trees like this for a few examples, your child will develop an intuitive understanding for how this works.

Coin flips and dice rolling Multiple flipping of a coin, or rolling of a die, are common examples of independent events.

A flip of a coin has no effect on the next flip. Each coin flip has two possibilities. If you flip a coin four times, the number of possible outcomes is

$$2 \times 2 \times 2 \times 2 = 2^4 = 16$$

Similarly, a roll of a die has no effect on other rolls. If you roll a six-sided die two times, the number of possible outcomes is

$$6 \times 6 = 6^2 = 36$$

License plates In California, license plates consist of a digit, followed by 3 letters, followed by 3 more digits. The 7 choices are independent and have no effect on each other. There are 10 choices for each digit, and 26 choices for each letter. So, the total number of possible license plates is

$$10 \times 26 \times 26 \times 26 \times 10 \times 10 \times 10 = 26^3 \times 10^4 = 175{,}760{,}000$$

Selecting with replacement An important example of independent choices is making *selections with replacement*.

Suppose you are making three-letter combinations with the letters a, b, c, and d. You are allowed to use each letter as many times as you like. You have three independent choices to make— your choice for any letter will have no effect on any of the other choices. Therefore, you have $4 \times 4 \times 4 = 4^3$ ways to do this.

This is called *selection with replacement* because selecting an item does not use it up—it is "replaced" and can be chosen again.

4.7 Independent vs. exclusive

 LESSON | Learning how to count independent and exclusive events.

Practice ▷ The following diagram shows one-way routes from city A to city D. The routes go through either city B or city C.

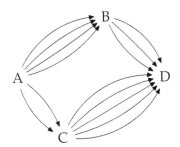

Suppose we want to count the number of ways of going from A to D that go through B. There are four ways to get from A to B, and there are 3 ways to get from B to D. The selections are independent, so there are $4 \times 3 = 12$ ways to do it.

Similarly, there are $2 \times 5 = 10$ ways of getting from A to D going through C.

There are two kinds of ways of going from A to D—either go through B, or through C. These are *exclusive* choices. You can do one or the other, and you cannot do both at one time. Therefore, the total number of ways of going from A to D is the sum of the number of ways of going through B, plus the number of ways of going through C. So, the total number is $12 + 10 = 22$.

Make lots of diagrams like this for your child to practice on. You can make diagrams with more intermediate cities between A and D, and you can even put more cities beyond D. Make sure that the routes are always one-way, and that there are no circular paths in your diagram.

4.8 Counting dependent events

LESSON Learning how to count dependent events.

Practice ▷ **Creating 2-letter words** Suppose you are making 2-letter words from the four letters a, b, c, and d. Each letter may be used at most once in each word. That is, once the letter is selected for use in a word, it is not replaced and cannot be used again.

You have four choices for selecting the first letter. After the first choice, there are three letters left to choose the second letter. This gives a total of $4 \times 3 = 12$ ways to form the words.

A tree is a good way to illustrate how this works.

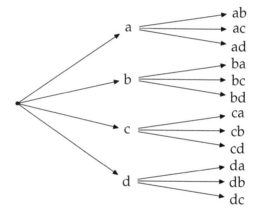

Selecting 4 class officers A class with 25 students needs to select 4 class officers—a president, vice president, secretary, and treasurer. In how many ways can this be done?

A student can be in only one office. The selection of a student for an office will reduce the choices available for other offices. Starting with the president, there are 25 students available. Once the president is picked, there are 24 students available for vice president. After these two have been picked, there are 23 choices for the secretary. Finally, after selecting the first three, there are 22 possibilities for treasurer. The number of ways to do this is

$$25 \times 24 \times 23 \times 22 = 303{,}600$$

Selecting without replacement The previous two examples are cases in which items are selected from a group, and after an item is selected it is not available because it is not replaced. This is called *selection without replacement*.

In general, if you are selecting k things without replacement from n things, you have n choices for selecting the first item, $n - 1$ choices for selecting the second, $n - 2$ for the third, and so on until k items have been selected.

Permuting a group of distinct objects Suppose you have a group of objects, and you want to count all the possible ways of rearranging them. These are called the *permutations* of the set of objects.

This is a special case of selecting k things without replacement from n things. Permutations count the number of ways of selecting all n things without replacement from n things.

For example, you might have 5 pictures to present, and you want to count how many different orders they can be presented in. This is the same kind of problem that was just discussed, namely, 5 things are being selected without replacement from a group of 5 things.

As before, you have 5 pictures to choose to be first, 4 pictures for second, 3 pictures for third, 2 pictures for fourth, and 1 for the fifth. So, the number of choices is

$$5 \times 4 \times 3 \times 2 \times 1 = 120$$

Practicing Beyond the examples given earlier in this section, there are a great many sources for creating permutation problems in day-to-day circumstances.

As an example, talk about the number of ways of putting 8 books on a shelf. Change that a little by putting only 5 of those 8 books on a small shelf. Talk about the number of ways of seating 6 people in a row of chairs, in a car, or seating them around a table. As another example, count things having to do with clothes, such as counting the number of ways that 12 team jerseys can be worn by 6 people on a team.

4.9 Independent and dependent events

 | Learning rules for independent and dependent probabilities.

Practice ▷ **Two independent events** Events are *independent* if they do not influence each other in any way.

> **RULE**   If A and B are independent events, then the probability that both events happen is the product of their probabilities:
>
> $P(A \text{ and } B) = P(A) \times P(B)$

For example, let A be the event of getting less than 3 on a die, and let B be the event of getting heads from a coin flip. The two events do not affect one another, so the probability that they will both happen is

$$P(A) \times P(B) = \frac{2}{6} \times \frac{1}{2} = \frac{1}{6}$$

Two dependent events Now, suppose that events A and B have some effect on each other. Their probabilities will no longer simply multiply—the second event, B in this case, must be adjusted to assume that the first event has already happened.

> **RULE**   If A and B are dependent events, then
>
> $P(A \text{ and } B) =$
> $P(A) \times P(B \text{ given that } A \text{ happened})$

For example, what is the probability of picking two cards from a deck of cards and having them both be spades?

Let A be the event of getting a spade for the first card, and B be the event of getting a spade for the second card. These are dependent events because what occurs during the first event affects what happens in the second event.

There are 13 spades out of the 52 cards, so

$$P(A) = \frac{13}{52} = \frac{1}{4}$$

If we assume that A has happened, then one spade has been removed from the deck. So, there are 12 spades among the 51 cards remaining.

$$P(B \text{ given that } A \text{ happened}) = \frac{12}{51} = \frac{4}{17}$$

The probability that both cards are spades is

$$P(A) \times P(B \text{ given that } A \text{ happened}) = \frac{1}{4} \times \frac{4}{17} = \frac{1}{17}$$

Practicing Use examples from previous sections to provide ways for your child to practice these ideas.

Any example from Section 4.6: *Counting independent events* will form the basis for a probability problem involving independent events. For example, what is the probability of creating a word that rhymes with "bad" when creating 3-letter words as was done at the start of that section? A word choice will rhyme with "bad" if it starts with any letter, its second letter is an "a," and its last letter is a "d." The probability is

$$\frac{3}{3} \times \frac{1}{2} \times \frac{1}{2} = \frac{1}{4}$$

For dependent events, use examples from Section 4.8: *Counting dependent events*. For example, what is the probability of getting two kings when selecting two cards from a deck of cards? The probability of getting a king for the first card is $\frac{4}{52}$. The probability of getting a king on the second card, given that a king was drawn for the first card, is $\frac{3}{51}$. Therefore, the probability is

$$\frac{4}{52} \times \frac{3}{51} = \frac{1}{13} \times \frac{1}{17} = \frac{1}{221}$$

4.10   Factorials

LESSON | Learning about factorials.

This section develops formulas useful for the material in Section 4.8: *Counting dependent events*. That section should be mastered first in order to have a rich set of problems to practice on.

Practice▷ **Factorials** In counting problems we frequently end up multiplying a sequence of numbers. A special symbol was created to make this easier to write. In this connection, the symbol "!" is called *factorial*.

> **MATH WORDS** The value of *n factorial*, written as *n!*, is:
>
> $n! = n \times (n-1) \times \cdots \times 1.$
>
> Also, $0! = 1$.

For example, $5! = 5 \times 4 \times 3 \times 2 \times 1 = 120$.

Permutations In Section 4.8: *Counting dependent events*, we calculated that the number of ways of permuting 5 pictures was

$$5 \times 4 \times 3 \times 2 \times 1 = 120$$

That is, the number of ways to permute 5 things is 5!. In general, the number of ways of permuting n things is $n!$.

Factorials divide each other Children usually enjoy how quickly factorials become quite large. Another fun thing about factorials is the way they evenly divide each other. For example, when dividing 5! by 3! there is a lot of canceling

$$\frac{5!}{3!} = \frac{5 \times 4 \times \cancel{3} \times \cancel{2} \times \cancel{1}}{\cancel{3} \times \cancel{2} \times \cancel{1}} = 5 \times 4 = 20$$

This property of factorials makes them useful in representing the answers to many different kinds of counting calculations. For example, in Section 4.8: *Counting dependent events* we counted the number of ways of selecting 4 class officers from a class of 25 students as:

$$25 \times 24 \times 23 \times 22$$

We can use factorials to rewrite this as:

$$25 \times 24 \times 23 \times 22 = \frac{25!}{21!}$$

When your child does problems involving *selecting without replacement*, have your child practice writing the answers using factorials.

Why does 0! = 1? If you use the traditional definition of factorials, as I gave it earlier, it is quite mysterious that 0! should equal 1. Mathematically, it is important that 0! = 1. There are several possible explanations you can use.

My favorite is that when you calculate a multiplicative thing such as a factorial, you should start your calculation with the number that has no effect under multiplication: the number 1. Calculate the factorial of a whole number by started with 1, and then multiplying it by 1, and then 2, and so on up to the number. For example,

$$5! = 1 \times 1 \times 2 \times 3 \times 4 \times 5 = 120$$

If you do that, then 2! = 1 × 1 × 2 = 2, 1! = 1 × 1 = 1, and 0! = 1.

Another way to explain it is using the idea that the number of ways of permuting n things is $n!$. Using that, there is exactly 1 way to permute nothing (just leave nothing as is), so that gives 0! = 1.

A final way to explain it is to use the relationship that we want $n! = n \times (n-1)!$, as much as it is possible. Putting $n = 1$ in this formula gives 1! = 1 × 0!.

4.11 Probability examples

LESSON | Seeing more examples of probability.

Practice ▷   Bringing up probability while playing games is a good way to show its usefulness to your child. Many children's games use dice. I will talk about Parcheesi, but the ideas are general.

There are lots of opportunities to choose where to let the playing pieces end up in Parcheesi. Often, you want to be in a good position to take somebody, or to avoid being taken.

When you roll two dice, there are $6 \times 6 = 36$ possible rolls.

What is the probability of getting a 7? There are 6 ways of getting a 7, namely $1 + 6$, $2 + 5$, $3 + 4$, $4 + 3$, $5 + 2$, and $6 + 1$. Therefore, the probability of getting a 7 is $\frac{6}{36} = \frac{1}{6}$.

There are two ways of getting a 3, so the probability is $\frac{2}{36} = \frac{1}{18}$.

In general, 7 is the most likely sum, and the numbers become less likely as you move up or down from 7.

One aspect that makes Parcheesi tricky is that a move can use part of a double, and doubles are surprisingly likely. There are 6 ways to get a double, so the probability of it happening is $\frac{6}{36} = \frac{1}{6}$.

A 5 is required on either die, or as a sum, in order to move a piece out of the home area. Sometimes a player will fail at this for several rolls. This is usually accompanied by grumbling about being unlucky. What is the probability of not getting a 5 after 3 rolls?

The rolls are independent events, so the probabilities multiply. There are 21 ways of not getting a 5 on either die or as a sum, so the probability is $\frac{21}{36} = \frac{7}{12}$. The probability of not getting a 5 two times in a row is

$$\left(\frac{7}{12}\right)^2$$

which is approximately $\frac{1}{3}$. It really is not particularly unlucky to take more than 2 rolls to get a piece out.

CHAPTER **5**

Statistics and Graphing

Statistics is the art of understanding, modeling, and describing a set of data. When there are 20, 30, or more numbers, it is very difficult to look at just the numbers on a page and see patterns and trends. Statistics attempts to simplify the data set, so that its characteristics are more easily understood and worked with.

Averages are a powerful tool for summarizing a data set. The aim is to come up with one number, or a small group of numbers, that tells much of the story of the data. I describe the standard averages, and talk about how to use box and whisker plots to display the five-number summary.

I go through some standard techniques to use if you want to look at all of the data. Ordering the data is the simplest and most basic way to organize the data.

Putting the data into organized tables makes it easier to understand. Stem and leaf tables display all of the data in a compact form. Frequency tables and histograms are a good middle ground between showing all of the data and summarizing it.

People are very strong at understanding pictures. At a glance we can take in a tremendous amount of information from a visual scene. Graphs and charts take advantage of that skill to show a great deal of data in an understandable manner.

The sections of this chapter describe an array of statistical tools. The way to make these tools come alive for your child is to look at real data sets from your child's life. Pull up old height and weight information from your child's lifetime and make a graph of it. If you have recorded measurements that were done for science, or just for practicing measuring, use statistics to analyze and display the information. If your child is wondering about the weather, sports data, information about people, or whatever else may be of interest, use those occasions to practice these techniques.

5.1 Averages

LESSON

Learning about data averages.

The goal of an average is to summarize a data set in one number. If you are told that a test in school has a median score of 87, you immediately know that it is a much easier test than one that has a median score of 75. Three averages that are discussed frequently in statistics are the mean, median, and mode.

Range, minimum, and maximum The *maximum* is the largest data element, and the *minimum* is the smallest element. The *range* is the difference between the maximum and minimum. Sometimes range is used to refer to the interval from the minimum to the maximum, rather than the difference.

Mean The *mean* is the sum of all of the data divided by how many items of data there are. This is also called the *arithmetic average* of the data. If someone asks for the "average" of a data set, this is usually what they want.

Median and quartiles This discussion assumes the data has been put into a list that is ordered from smallest to largest.

The *median* is the middle data item in the ordered list. The median breaks a data set into two pieces—half of the data will come before the median, and half after it. If the number of data items is odd, the median is the middle term. If the number of data items is even, the median is the mean of the two middle terms.

The quartiles break the data set into four pieces. The *first quartile, Q1,* is the median of all of the data elements listed before the median. The *third quartile, Q3,* is the median of all of the data elements listed after the median. The median is also called the *second quartile, Q2.*

Box and whisker charts The *five-number summary* consists of: minimum, Q1, median, Q3, and maximum. These five numbers capture a large amount of information about the spread of values in a data set.

Box and whisker charts are used to display the five-number summary. A rectangular box is drawn on a number line starting at Q1 and ending at Q3. A line is drawn in the box where the median is. At each end of the box a line is drawn to lines where the minimum and maximum are (the whiskers).

Here is a box and whisker chart for the five-number summary 7, 10, 12, 20, 23.

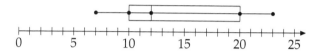

Mode The *mode* is the data item that occurs the most frequently in a data set. This is the favorite average to use for non-numerical data. When a report is given on which song is a school's favorite, the report will use the mode.

If there is a tie, it is possible for a data set to have more than one mode. If there are a lot of ties, especially if every data element occurs just once, the data set is said to not have a mode.

Example Apply these ideas to the number of home runs hit by Hank Aaron in each of his major league seasons.

13 27 26 44 30 39 40 34 45 44 24 32 44 39 29 44 38 47 34 40 20 12 10

Start by putting these in order:

10 12 13 20 24 26 27 29 30 32 34 34 38 39 39 40 40 44 44 44 44 45 47

The minimum is 10, and the maximum is 47. The values go from 10 to 47, so the range is $47 - 10 = 37$.

There are two 34's, two 39's, two 40's, and four 44's. So the mode is 44. If you were to pick a year at random, the most likely number of home runs would be 44.

Hank Aaron hit 755 home runs over 23 seasons, which gives a mean of $\frac{755}{23} = 32\frac{19}{23}$.

The middle term of 23 terms is the 12th, so the median is 34.

To compute Q1, look at the terms before the 12th:

10 12 13 20 24 26 27 29 30 32 34

This has 11 entries. Its median is the sixth entry, so Q1 = 26.

To compute Q3, look at the terms after the 12th:

38 39 39 40 40 44 44 44 44 45 47

This has 11 entries. Its median is the sixth entry, so Q3 = 44.

The five-number summary is 10, 26, 34, 44, 47. The box and whisker chart for this is:

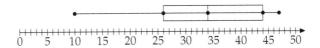

This box and whisker chart makes it very easy to see certain things at a glance: he hit between 10 and 47 home runs every year, in 50 percent of the years he hit between 26 and 44 home runs, and the median year of his home run production had 34 home runs.

5.2 Tables of data

 LESSON | Learning about tables of data.

Practice ⟫   There are several ways of creating lists or tables for a data set.

Ordering One of the most basic techniques is to order the data. In the Hank Aaron home run example in the last section, the first step was to take the raw data:

> 13 27 26 44 30 39 40 34 45 44 24 32 44 39 29 44 38 47 34 40 20 12 10

and put it in order:

> 10 12 13 20 24 26 27 29 30 32 34 34 38 39 39 40 40 44 44 44 44 45 47

Ordering the data makes it quite a bit easier to understand.

Stem and leaf chart A stem and leaf chart is a way of taking ordered data and making it even easier to understand. Usually the data are rounded so that they consist entirely of whole numbers.

Each data entry has one entry as a leaf. The leaves are usually the ones digits from the numbers, and the stems are the higher-order digits.

Here is a stem and leaf chart for Hank Aaron's home runs. The top entry is 10, where 1 is the stem and 0 is the leaf. As another example, the entry 38 has a stem of 3 and a leaf of 8.

Stem	Leaf
1	0 2 3
2	0 4 6 7 9
3	0 2 4 4 8 9 9
4	0 0 4 4 4 4 5 7

Frequency tables A *frequency table*, or a *frequency distribution table*, shows how many times a type of entry occurs. The table sometimes has a column for doing a tally as the data is recorded, and also a column for a cumulative count of all the rows up to that point. Here is a frequency table for the Hank Aaron data set:

Range	Tally	Count	Cum. Count
10 – 19	|||	3	3
20 – 29	|||||	5	8
30 – 39	|||||||	7	15
40 – 49	||||||||	8	23

Histogram and pictograph Other ways to show the frequency of data items are to use a pictograph or histogram.

Pictographs use pictures to show the amount or size of the data. Suppose you want to count the fruit in your kitchen. Use one column in the pictograph for each kind of fruit, and a picture of a piece of fruit for each piece you find. Suppose you had three apples, two oranges, and five bananas.

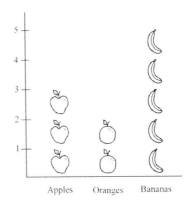

Another kind of pictograph uses the same idea, only instead of indicating the quantity using separate symbols, it shows the quantity by scaling up the picture of the symbol. For example, suppose there were 4 oranges and 1 apple. Then the single image of an orange would be approximately 4 times as large as the apple.

Pictographs are a good display to use with young children. The pictures of the objects make the representation less abstract.

Another way to show this same information is to use a histogram. A histogram is very similar to a pictograph, only now the quantity is shown using the length of a bar.

As your child becomes accustomed to bar graphs with pictures, use filled-in columns where the height of the column indicates the value. To make this transition easier, use pictures that are all the same size. If the pictures are the same size, then the number of pictures will directly relate to the height of the column.

While changing to filled-in columns is a big conceptual change, it can be a relatively minor visual change if you have been careful with the picture sizes.

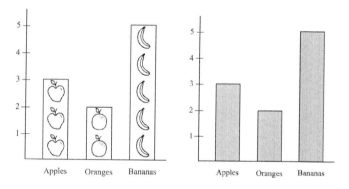

Here is a histogram showing Hank Aaron's home run data:

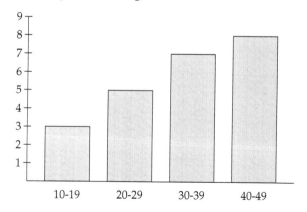

5.3 Graphs of data

 LESSON | Learning about graphing data.

Practice People are outstanding at seeing patterns and trends in visual information. Graphing takes advantage of that ability by translating lists of numbers into visual information. Graphs make it much easier to compare quantities, see trends, and recognize relationships.

One way to practice graphing is to combine the activity of graphing with doing a daily measurement of something. For example, make a daily line graph of the high and low temperatures for each day. Graph how far one of your cars is driven each day or week. Graph how much money is spent for groceries each week.

Bar graphs These graphs are a natural place for your child to start learning about graphing data. Each item or category is associated with a rectangular bar whose length is proportional to the size of the data. This proportionality makes the relationship with the data more natural, and less abstract.

The last section looked at displaying frequency data using pictographs and histograms. Histograms are bar graphs where the data displayed is frequency information.

Here is a bar graph showing the number of hobbies five children have:

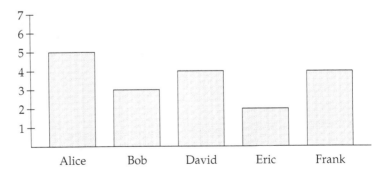

Line graphs Once your child is at ease with bar graphs, transition to
line graphs. Emphasize the similarity between line graphs and
bar graphs by making the first line graphs with a dot or line
at the top of where the bar would normally be in a bar graph,
without drawing in the rest of the column.

For a while, the line graphs that your child draws should have
the values along the left side of the graph start with 0. As your
child grows more practiced with these, experiment with graphs
whose vertical values start at various numbers, and see what
different effects are produced.

Here is an example of a graph of the number of children at school
each day for a week. Each column is labeled at the bottom with
the day of the week. Suppose that the five days have 28, 29, 32,
31, and 32 children.

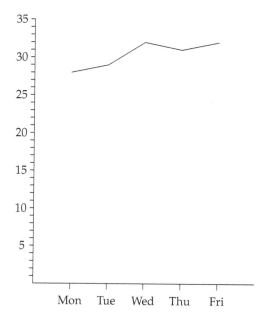

Starting the vertical numbering at 25 makes it easier to see the
important differences in the data. However, the height no longer
directly corresponds to the value of the data.

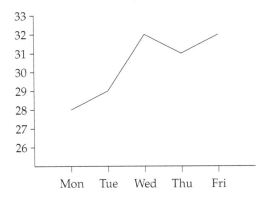

Questions to ask Using either of the last line graphs as a reference, here are some of the kinds of questions you can pose to your child: On which day were there the fewest or the most children? Which two days had the same value? Between which days did the number of children increase/decrease?

Pie charts These charts are also called circle graphs. For these graphs, a circle is broken up into slices, where the size of each slice is proportional to the size of the data.

Suppose you want to use a pie chart to show the amount of fruit you have in your kitchen. You find you have 4 oranges, 1 apple, and 3 pears. In a pie chart, each item is given the same fraction of the circle that it is as a fraction of the whole collection. For example, there are 3 pears and a total of 8 pieces of fruit. So the pears would be represented by a slice that is $\frac{3}{8}$ of the whole circle.

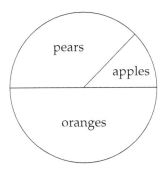

These graphs are good for showing the relative size of the pieces that make up a whole item. Representing budgets with these charts works well, because it emphasizes the role each piece plays in the whole budget. For example, you could graph how much money your child spends, and have slices for the various categories like entertainment and toys.

These graphs can be hard for a child to create. Until your child is proficient dividing 360 degrees into complicated fractional parts, keep any examples simple so that they involve relatively small fractions, such as fourths or eighths.

Scatter plots Scatter plots are useful for displaying data collected from an experiment or study.

Here are the high temperatures on a recent day for cities in the San Diego area. Each data entry has two numbers—the first is the number of miles from the coast, and the second is the high temperature for the day.

$$(1, 73) \ (6, 78) \ (8, 85) \ (11, 82) \ (14, 86) \ (15, 90) \ (20, 95)$$

To make a scatter plot, these pairs are plotted on a coordinate plane as described in Section 6.8: *Coordinate plane*. The scatter plot makes it clear how the temperature increases with the distance from the coast.

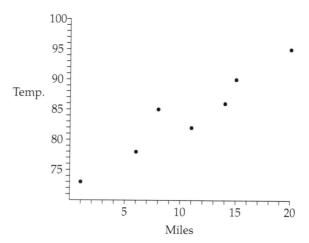

CHAPTER 6

Geometry

Beginning geometry is all about drawing, creating, and playing with all sorts of shapes. In addition to this interactive and playful sense of objects, part of the mathematics to be learned is the names and descriptions of shapes. This builds an awareness in your child of these objects, and it creates a vocabulary that your child can use to think about and discuss geometry in everyday things.

Traditional playing with blocks is a natural and good source of experience with geometry. Seeing how blocks fit together, and don't fit together, is one of the best ways for your child to learn the characteristics of various shapes and sizes. The famous architect Frank Lloyd Wright as a child played with a special set of blocks designed by Friedrich Froebel, and he credits this experience with giving him insights into geometry, mathematics, and architecture.

Shapes Start at a young age by teaching your child the names for basic shapes such as triangles, rectangles, squares, and circles. This teaching is not done in any formal way: just use the names when referring to everyday things and your child will learn them.

As your child is ready, transition to some of the names for more complex shapes, and start using some of the concepts introduced later in this chapter. Make sure your child's toys include a wide variety of shapes to play with, including shapes with more than four sides.

Vocabulary games There is a lot of terminology needed to be able to talk about geometric ideas, and it can seem somewhat endless at times. There are some ways to make a game out of learning all of this vocabulary.

One way is to have a scavenger hunt. Start by making a list of geometric ideas you are searching for. This can be names of two-dimensional or three-dimensional shapes, or it can be features such as having symmetries or right angles. The first person to find all of the items on the list wins.

Another game to play is Concentration. Make a set of cards that have vocabulary words and drawings of shapes. The cards are placed face down, and players take turns turning over a pair of cards looking for a match. If there is a match, the cards are kept and the player continues. If the cards do not match, the cards are turned back face down, and the next player goes.

Concentration can be played in many ways. One way is to have two cards for each idea, and a match is an exact match— word with word, drawing with drawing, or word with drawing. Another way is to have just one copy of most cards, and matches are made by being able to name one (or possibly two) features the two cards have in common. For example, a square and a rectangle might match because they both have right angles and are quadrilaterals.

Yet another way to play with this is to use a collection of shapes. Use blocks already made into interesting shapes, or use pieces of stiff cardboard you have cut into various shapes. With eyes closed, have your child choose a piece from a container and describe it using the new vocabulary.

Patterns, symmetries, and transformations One way for your child to see the world through geometric eyes is to look for symmetries and the effects of transformations (these are described in sections 6.9 and 6.10). Thinking about geometry from this point of view teaches your child to see things not just as they are, but to explore what can happen to them as they are mentally moved around and manipulated.

Several of the sections of this chapter describe patterns and designs that your child can play with and explore. You can look at or construct tiling patterns and drawing designs. You can find pictures of patterns in weaving, pottery, and architecture. Many of these designs and patterns are rich playgrounds for exploring how shapes interact, and most have interesting symmetries.

Activities This chapter is filled with terminology and lists of properties. You should not view this as a large collection of facts to be memorized and recited. Try to maintain the view that these are related concepts that can be discovered, dipped into, and played with.

A good way to bring these ideas alive is to engage in related activities. Section 6.4: *Taking directions* describes a game for practicing basic distances and directions. For those willing to dip into some programming, there is the LOGO environment in which beautiful pictures can be created using elementary geometry ideas.

Another activity is making straight-edge and compass constructions. These can be fun, but they are somewhat limited in number. You can extend these constructions by using a straight-edge and compass to create geometric designs for drawings. A wonderful, dynamic way to play with these ideas is to use either of two software programs designed for this purpose: *GeoGebra* or *Geometer's Sketchpad*.   These ideas are discussed further in Section 6.16: *Straight-edge and compass*.

Graph theory The graph theory section at the end of the chapter creates a very different geometric world for your child to play in. There are a number of graph theory related puzzles that your child can play with.

Shameless plug The book *Introduction to Geometry*, which is written by Richard Rusczyk and published by the Art of Problem Solving, covers the topics of this chapter in much more depth, and it covers many topics that are natural extensions. The book can even serve as a textbook for a full geometry course. The interested child will find it an excellent way to enjoy more material on this subject.

6.1 Designs and patterns

  Exploring geometric designs and patterns.

Practice▶ Noticing and playing with geometric designs and patterns is a wonderful way to deepen your child's understanding of geometry. Whether it's putting together a jigsaw puzzle, noticing tile patterns in a house, looking at rows of plants in an orchard, or seeing how seeds grow in a sunflower, there are geometric shapes and patterns all around for your child to have fun with.

Jigsaw puzzles Seeing how two puzzle pieces match, or looking for a missing piece, is great practice with shapes.

Tiles and pattern blocks Colored tiles that fit together to make flat patterns provide lots of practice with geometry, as well as being lots of fun in their own right. A bucket of blocks, called "pattern blocks" in educational supply catalogues, is a good source of such tiles.

Zillij, a Moroccan art using ceramic tiles to produce beautiful geometric patterns, has been practiced in Morocco for 12 centuries. Look these up online to see many fabulous designs. Encourage your child to draw simplified versions of some of the designs.

There are many fun pieces of software available for making tilings, patterns, and symmetries. For example, "Taprats" is a free Java applet available on the web for making Islamic star patterns.

Tessellations A tessellation, also called a tiling, is a complete covering of a surface with a collection of geometric shapes. Most tessellations consist of a small collection of polygons used repeatedly to form a regular, or semi-regular, pattern.

There are many kinds of tessellations, starting with simple *regular tessellations*, going on to far more complex ones. A regular tessellation is made up of identical regular polygons, and there are only three such designs—using triangles, squares, or hexagons. Some examples are a chessboard covered by squares and a honeycomb covered with hexagons.

Playing with pattern blocks is an easy way to create tessellations. Have your child explore which blocks fit together to form repeating patterns. You can combine this exploration with the topic in Section 6.3: *Angles*, which discusses the role 360° plays in tilings. Tessellations can be produced using transformations, and usually contain many symmetries, so there is a good connection with the material in Section 6.9: *Transformations* and Section 6.10: *Symmetry*.

For more fun with tessellations, look into tessellations using unusual shapes. Also, experiment with the nonperiodic tilings created by British mathematician Sir Roger Penrose. One of his examples uses just two shapes to create tilings that have no repeating pattern. Look up *Penrose Tilings* on the internet and have your child make such a tiling by cutting out many copies of these two tiles using different colors of stiff paper, and then fit them together to form beautiful designs.

The drawings of artist M. C. Escher are a lot of fun. Many of his drawings use imaginative tilings of interesting shapes that change from one part of the drawing to the next.

Tangram Tangram is a Chinese game created from a square cut into seven special pieces, as shown below on the left. The challenge is to put these seven pieces together to form a given shape, or a shape of your own. Do an internet search for *tangram puzzle* to try some.

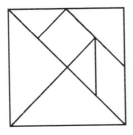 

Pentominoes A Pentomino set consists of 12 pieces, as shown above on the right, each of which is made up of five squares. As in Tangram, the challenge is to take these pieces and put them together to form a given shape.

Misc. designs There are a great many kinds of designs that people have created to make their world more beautiful. Many of these would be difficult for you to do, but all can be interesting to study.

Rugs from different regions have beautiful designs and very different characteristics. Oriental and Mideastern rugs have a rich tradition of complicated and subtle patterns. Navajo rugs often have simpler patterns, and their simplicity can make them easier for your child to spot symmetries and to make drawings similar in style.

Knot designs are an interesting example of designs that are not based on polygons. Celtic knot designs have a long history—look into the designs in the *Book of Kells* from over a thousand years ago. You can also investigate knot designs from other regions, such as from Russia and Japan.

Spiral designs Spiral designs occur frequently in nature. For example, you can find them in the seeds in sunflowers, the hexagonal scales on the surface of a pineapple, and in the way bracts grow on a pine cone.

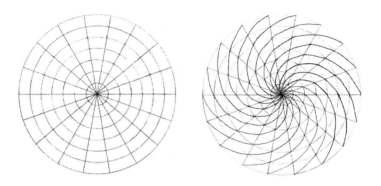

Your child can create spiral patterns using the following method. First, draw a series of concentric circles, and put in straight lines evenly spaced around the circles. Then, connect the intersection points using a spacing rule of your choosing. Increase the number of circles and radii to make more detailed spirals.

Architecture Architecture is a rich source of geometry and patterns. Look at the large details of buildings and bridges to see lots of examples of how polygons and other shapes fit together.

There are many beautiful buildings around the world that contain magnificent patterns and designs in their small detail work. The Taj Mahal is one famous example, and the Alhambra Palace in Granada, Spain, is another. Look these up on the web and explore the patterns with your child.

6.2 Points, lines, and planes

 Learning about basic geometric shapes—points, lines, and angles.

Practice ▶ This section describes a number of basic geometric objects and terms. This terminology is pretty dry on its own, but it will be used in discussing more interesting shapes in the sections to come.

Use these terms to talk about the things you see, especially your child's blocks and toys. This practice will make these names become part of how your child sees the world.

Point Mathematicians use abstract definitions of a *point*, but for our purposes a point, A, will be a small dot made by a pencil or marker on a piece of paper.

Line, segment, and ray A *line* is a collection of points going infinitely far forward and backward, straight in a given direction from a point. To refer to the line given above you would write $\overleftrightarrow{BC}$.

Three or more points that lie on the same line are called *collinear*.

A *line segment* is a portion of a line that starts and ends at two points on a line. It is named after its endpoints, $\overline{BC}$. Pieces of uncooked spaghetti make good examples of line segments. *Bisecting* a line segment means to cut it in half.

A *ray* is like a ray of sunshine—it starts at a point, D in this example, goes through point E, and then continues on forever in one direction in a straight line. It is written $\overrightarrow{DE}$.

Plane A *plane* is an infinite flat surface. Think of this as a flat sheet of paper that goes on forever in all directions.

Line designs Explore making line designs with your child. These are made up of a sequence of line segments, each of which is created using a small change from the previous segment. These can be made by drawing lines on paper, or by placing nails in a stiffer surface and connecting the nails with pieces of string.

Make these by starting with a frame. The frame might be a simple right angle, triangle, or square. Once you have the frame, mark the sides of the frame with evenly spaced points that will be the endpoints of the segments. Pick two points to connect for the first segment, and then keep moving both endpoints one space to create the remaining segments.

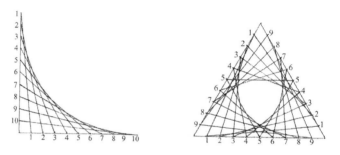

If your child enjoys these a lot, try some more complicated frames. The frames can have lots of sides. They can even involve curves, as in my design below.

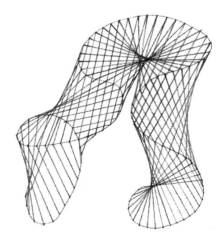

6.3 Angles

 Learning terms for basic geometric shapes having to do with angles.

Practice ▶   This is another section of terminology, this time having to do with angles. Many of these terms, such as *complementary* and *adjacent*, are not very important for beginning geometry, but exposing your child to them will ease the transition later on when your child starts doing more sophisticated things with geometry.

Definition An *angle* is formed by two rays that have the same end-point. The angle shown below is written ∠G or ∠FGH or ∠HGF. The common endpoint, G, is always written in the middle.

Measure The size of an angle is usually described in degrees, and is measured with a protractor. *Bisecting* an angle means to cut it into two equal angles, each half the measure of the original. In the drawing, $\overrightarrow{GB}$ bisects the 60-degree angle ∠FGH into two 30-degree angles.

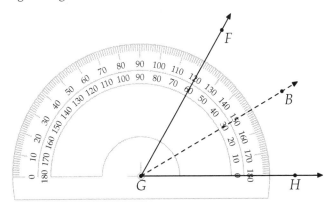

Acute, right, obtuse, and straight An angle is called a *right angle* if the measure of the angle is 90 degrees. Right angles are often marked with a little square in the corner of the angle.

An angle is called a *straight angle* if the two rays lie on a line and go in opposite directions. The measure of a straight angle is 180 degrees.

If the measure of an angle is between 90 and 180 degrees, then it is called *obtuse*. If the measure of an angle is between 0 and 90 degrees, then it is called *acute*.

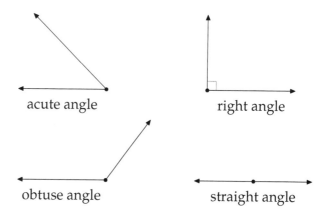

Complementary If the sum of the measures of two angles is 90 degrees, then the angles are called *complementary*. A very common way that complementary angles occur is in triangles that have a right angle. The other two angles in such a triangle will be complementary.

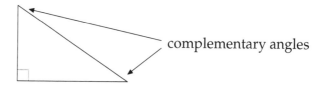

Supplementary and linear pair If the sum of the measures of two angles is 180 degrees, then the angles are called *supplementary*. If you take a point on a line and draw a ray from the point going away from the line, the two angles formed are called a *linear pair*. Linear pairs of angles are supplementary.

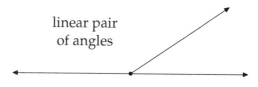

Adjacent Two angles are said to be *adjacent* if they have the same endpoint, have a ray in common, and their interiors do not overlap.

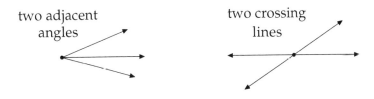

two adjacent angles

two crossing lines

When two lines cross, they form adjacent angles that are linear pairs.

Mirrors and lenses Have your child play with angles by investigating reflected and refracted light beams using mirrors and lenses.

When light reflects off a mirror, the angle it leaves from the mirror is the same as the angle it comes in. This reflection principle is similar to what happens on a pool table. I am sure your child has tried to touch something by looking into a mirror, and realized that something was different about the image.

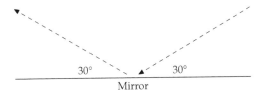

30°   30°

Mirror

The reflections become even more interesting to think about when two or more mirrors are involved. When two mirrors meet in a 90 degree corner, the images seen in them get reflected twice, and the reflected light rays leave on a path parallel to the incoming path.

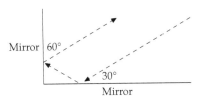

Mirror 60°

30°

Mirror

The material in Section 6.9: *Transformations* and Section 6.10: *Symmetry* connects well with mirror images, so you may want to do some of that with your child at this time.

Another experiment to do with light is to close one eye and look through a magnifying glass being held at arms length. All of the images are reversed! This has to do with the light rays crossing, as in the following suggestive diagram, which reverses all of the angles.

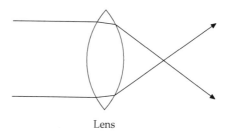

Lens

If your child is enjoying this investigation, look into how eyes and cameras work. Other lens systems that may be fun to look into are eyeglasses, magnifying lenses, telescopes, and microscopes.

Why tiles fit together If you have some tiling blocks, or if you have some tile work in your house, have your child use a protractor to measure the angles of the corners of the pieces. Your child's measurements of these angles should match up with the results mentioned later in this chapter—for example, that each angle of a regular triangle is 60°, that each angle of a square is 90°, and each angle of a regular hexagon is 120°.

Ask your child to predict whether a group of pieces will fit together without a gap. After some trial and error, help your child discover that the sum of the angles needs to be 360° for the pieces to fit tightly together without a gap.

6.4 Taking directions

 LESSON | Using direction commands to learn about distances and angles.

Practice ⟩➤ There is a wonderful activity you can do with your child that provides lots of practice with lines and angles. This is based on the computer language LOGO, but you do not need to know the first thing about computers to play this.

We play this with our children in our yard as a treasure hunt. One person hides a treasure, picks a starting point and a starting direction to face, and then hands the other person a set of directions.

There are four kinds of directions that can be given.

1. Go forward some number of steps or some measured distance. For example, "go forward 5 steps" or "go forward 8 feet." The person following directions moves forward this much in the direction he is facing, and remains facing in that direction.

2. Go backward some steps or distance. This is the same as going forward only moving backward. Do not change the direction that you are facing.

3. Turn right some number of degrees. The person following directions does not change location, but does change the direction he is facing. Start by only using 90 degrees until your child becomes comfortable with the game.

4. Turn left some number of degrees. This is similar to turning right.

That is all there is to it. Using step counts can be a bit tricky if people have different stride lengths. It is usually most fun if the person giving directions has to make up all of the directions in advance and writes them down. Then you get to see what crazy place in the yard the person following the directions ends up.

If you would like to learn more about LOGO, look at the *Turtle Geometry* reference in Section 11.3: *Books teaching math subjects* or the LOGO reference in Section 11.6: *Software programs*.

6.5 Two lines

 LESSON Learning geometric terms having to do with two lines in a plane.

Practice▷ Two lines in a plane either cross each other, or go in the same direction. Here is some terminology for those situations.

Parallel lines If two lines in a plane do not meet, they are said to be *parallel*. Straight railroad tracks are a great example of this.

A line which cuts across two other lines is called a *transversal*. In the diagram below, $\overleftrightarrow{JL}$ and $\overleftrightarrow{KM}$ are transversals to the parallel lines $\overleftrightarrow{JK}$ and $\overleftrightarrow{LM}$. Write $\overleftrightarrow{JK} \parallel \overleftrightarrow{LM}$ to indicate parallel lines.

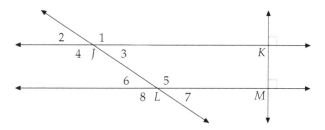

The eight angles formed by a transversal when it cuts a pair of parallel lines are all equal or supplementary to each other. In the diagram, angles 1, 4, 5, and 8 are equal, and angles 2, 3, 6, and 7 are equal. All of the angles in the first group are supplementary to all of the angles in the second group.

Perpendicular lines If two lines meet at right angles, they are called *perpendicular*. In the last diagram, $\overleftrightarrow{KM}$ is perpendicular to $\overrightarrow{JK}$ and $\overleftrightarrow{LM}$. This is written $\overleftrightarrow{KM} \perp \overrightarrow{JK}$ and $\overleftrightarrow{KM} \perp \overleftrightarrow{LM}$.

Challenge your child to find perpendicular lines around your home, or in any building you walk by. Most structures have lots of rectangles, and the sides of rectangles are perpendicular. Intersecting streets are often perpendicular.

Vertical angles Whenever two lines cross, four angles are created.

An adjacent pair of these angles is a linear pair, and the angles are supplementary. For example, ∠BAC and ∠CAD form a linear pair.

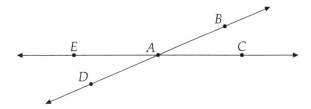

Within this group of four angles, a pair of opposite angles is called *vertical*. Notice that vertical angles are always equal. For example, ∠BAC and ∠DAE are equal vertical angles.

6.6 Plane figures

 | Learning terms having to do with plane figures.

Practice▷ **Plane and simple** A *plane figure* is a shape made up of straight and curved lines all lying in a plane. It is called a *simple figure* if the lines that make up the figure only intersect where they connect at their endpoints, and if all of the lines are connected together.

open
simple figure

not a
simple figure

Closed A simple figure is *closed* if it divides the plane into three distinct regions—one region which is inside the figure, another which is outside the figure, and the third is the figure itself.

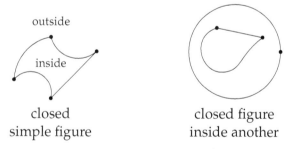

outside

inside

closed
simple figure

closed figure
inside another

Sprouts The Sprouts game described on page 212 in Chapter 10: *Learning Games and Activities* is an excellent game for practicing with curved figures and learning about insides and outsides.

Finding inside and outside Once your child understands about even and odd numbers, there is a fun way to tell whether a point is on the inside or outside of a closed figure.

One of you can draw an extremely complicated closed figure with a great deal of looping around in it. Take any point not on the figure and ask whether it is on the inside or outside of the figure. Of course, one way to answer that question is to carefully trace around the figure noticing which areas are actually on the outside of the figure.

A more enjoyable way to decide this is to draw a line from the point to somewhere outside the figure. Then, simply count the number of times this line crosses the figure. If there are an even number of crossings, then the point is on the outside, and if there are an odd number, then it must be on the inside. Try different lines from the same point and see how the number of crossings always varies by a multiple of two.

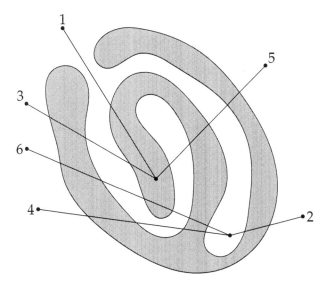

6.7 Similar and congruent shapes

LESSON | Learning about similar and congruent figures.

Your child will need to have mastered the material in Section 1.12: *Solving proportions* in the *Equations and Inequalities* Chapter, to work on ratio and proportion problems coming from similar figures.

Practice ▷ **Congruent** Two objects are called *congruent* if they have the same shape and size, that is, if they look the same. Whether the parts are angles or lengths, any pair of corresponding parts from congruent figures are the same. Production lines in factories create products that are congruent. If triangles *ABC* and *DEF* are congruent, this is written △*ABC* ≅ △*DEF*.

Similar One object is *similar* to a second if, by making it uniformly bigger or smaller, it becomes congruent to the second. Similar objects have the same shape, but not necessarily the same size. The corresponding angles in two similar objects will be the same. If triangles *ABC* and *GHI* are similar, this is written △*ABC* ~ △*GHI*. Two objects which are congruent are always similar.

The three triangles in the following diagram are similar, but only the first two are congruent.

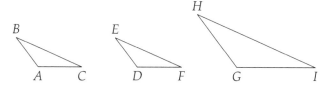

Order is important When specifying a similarity or congruence, be careful with the order when listing the corner points. For the diagram above, it is important to specify △*ABC* ≅ △*DEF*, and not △*ABC* ≅ △*EDF*, or some other matchup. Writing △*ABC* ≅ △*DEF* specifies six things—that angles ∠*A*, ∠*B*, and ∠*C* have the same measure as angles ∠*D*, ∠*E*, and ∠*F*, respectively, and that sides $\overline{AB}$, $\overline{BC}$, and $\overline{CA}$ have the same length as $\overline{DE}$, $\overline{EF}$, and $\overline{FD}$, respectively.

Same and different One point of using these terms is to give your child another way to describe how things look the same, and how they differ. For example, ask your child why it is that all squares are similar, but not all rectangles are. Talk about why all circles are similar to each other. Ask your child whether people are similar, and whether twins are congruent. When things are not similar, talk about what aspect of the shapes makes them different.

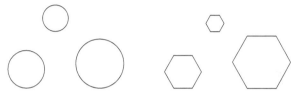

Maps An excellent example of similarity is a map. A map has a scale shown in the legend, showing that 1 inch on the map is the same as, say, 5 miles in the real world. Talk about how the shapes of streets, parks, and buildings on the map are similar to the real shapes they represent.

A fun way to practice this is to make a scale drawing of your house, your child's room, or the arrangement of furniture and shelves along a wall. Making these maps will also give your child lots of measuring practice. You might want to combine this with a project to rearrange or redecorate some portion of your house. If you are planning to put some play structures in your yard, your child can start by making a scale map of the yard and then you can take scale models of things and move them around the map.

If you are feeling ambitious, make a scale 3-dimensional model of some portion of your house or yard.

Scaling factor for similarity When two objects are similar, one of them will be a larger or smaller version of the shape of the other. This increase or decrease in size is called the *scaling factor* in going from one similar shape to the other.

For example, in going from a 10″ by 10″ square to a 30″ by 30″ square, the scaling factor is 3. In going from that same 10″ by 10″ square to a 5″ by 5″ square, the scaling factor is $\frac{1}{2}$.

Effect of scaling factor on other dimensions Let A be a 2″ by 3″ by 5″ box, and B be a 10″ by 15″ by 25″ box. The scaling factor in going from A to B is 5.

All of the corresponding lengths in B are 5 times as large as the ones in A. This includes all of the edges of the box, as well as the diagonals along the faces, and even the internal diagonals.

All of the corresponding areas in B are $25 = 5^2$ as large as the ones in A. For example, each face of B has an area 25 times as large as it is in A. All of the corresponding volumes in B are $125 = 5^3$ as large as the ones in A.

Have your child verify these relationships for areas and volumes by applying the formulas from Section 6.17: *Areas* and Section 6.20: *Volumes and surface areas*. Point out that each additional dimension will produce another factor of the scaling factor in the calculation.

Ratios and proportions Another way of looking at the scaling factor of similar objects is that it forces a constant ratio between lengths.

For example, consider two circles—M has radius 2″ and N has radius 6″. The scaling factor in going from M to N is 3.

$$3 = \frac{\text{radius of } M}{\text{radius of } N} = \frac{\text{diameter of } M}{\text{diameter of } N} = \frac{\text{circumference of } M}{\text{circumference of } N}$$

Consider the following two similar triangles, $\triangle ABC \sim \triangle DEF$.

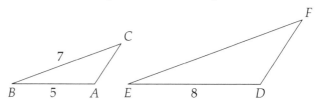

If you are asked to find the length of $\overline{EF}$, you will need to solve the following equation that describes this proportion

$$\frac{\text{length } \overline{ED}}{\text{length } \overline{BA}} = \frac{\text{length } \overline{EF}}{\text{length } \overline{BC}} \quad\Longrightarrow\quad \frac{8}{5} = \frac{\text{length } \overline{EF}}{7}$$

Solving equations of this type is discussed further in Section 1.12: *Solving proportions* in the *Equations and Inequalities* Chapter.

Using shadows to measure height Show your child how to measure the height of any tree or building on a sunny day. The right triangles formed by objects and their shadows at a given time will all be similar. Therefore, if you use a person whose height you know, and you measure the shadows of the person and a tree, you can get the height of the tree by solving the formula:

$$\frac{\text{person's height}}{\text{length of person's shadow}} = \frac{\text{tree's height}}{\text{length of tree's shadow}}$$

Golden Ratio The *golden ratio* is a famous ratio discovered by mathematicians in ancient Greece. A surprisingly large number of things in nature occur in terms of this ratio. For example, it shows up in the way leaves grow on a stem, bracts grow on a pine cone, and seeds grow in a sunflower.

The Greeks felt the golden ratio was aesthetically pleasing and made use of it in their architecture. Renaissance painters used it in the ratios of objects in their paintings.

One way to describe the golden ratio is as the ratio of the sides of a *golden rectangle*. A golden rectangle has the property that when you cut a square from one end of it you get a new rectangle that is similar to the original rectangle and whose sides have the same ratio. In the picture below, the ratio 1.618/1.0 of the sides of the large rectangle is the same as the ratio 1.0/0.618 of the sides of the smaller rectangle created by removing the 1 by 1 square.

Golden Rectangle

The Fibonacci sequence is closely tied to the golden ratio. The rule for creating this sequence is to start with two 1's, and then add the last two terms in the sequence to make the next term. For example, $1 + 1 = 2$, $1 + 2 = 3$, $2 + 3 = 5$, and so on.

$$1, 1, 2, 3, 5, 8, 13, 21, 34, 55, 89, 144, \ldots$$

The ratio of each pair of terms in the Fibonacci sequence approximates the golden ratio value of about 1.618. The farther you go in the sequence, the closer the ratio gets. Here are the first few ratios:

$$\frac{3}{2} = 1.5 \quad \frac{5}{3} \approx 1.666 \quad \frac{8}{5} = 1.6 \quad \frac{13}{8} = 1.625 \quad \frac{21}{13} \approx 1.615$$

A fun activity to do with your child is to count the number of spirals going in one direction on a pine cone or a pineapple. This number will almost always be a number in the Fibonacci sequence.

Another fun activity to do with your child is to measure a person's total height, and divide that by the height of the belly button from the ground. This should be very close to the golden ratio. If you have fun with this, there are a number of other body measurements that approximate the golden ratio—you can look these up on the internet by searching on *golden ratio* and *body*.

6.8 Coordinate plane

LESSON Learning about coordinate planes, and plotting points on them.

 One way to describe where you are relative to another place is to say how far east or west you are, and then how far north or south you are. The coordinate plane works in the same way.

Origin, *x*-axis, *y*-axis At the center of things is a special point called the *origin*. Running through the origin is a line called the *x-axis*. Running through the origin in the perpendicular direction is a line called the *y-axis*.

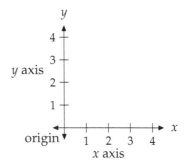

The *x*-axis is labeled as a number line with 0 at the origin, and with numbers increasing to the right. The *y*-axis is also labeled as a number line with 0 at the origin, and with numbers increasing going up. Since this book does not cover negative numbers, I will gloss over the negative sides of the *x*-axis and *y*-axis.

Buying a pad of graphing paper is a good idea for playing around with this. This will give your child an accurate and effortless way to play with these ideas.

If you have access to a big cement or asphalt area, draw a large coordinate plane on it using sidewalk chalk. Having your child race around to various yelled-out coordinates is a fun activity that helps make the concepts real.

Plotting points A point on the coordinate plane is described by an
ordered pair, (x, y).

Find the location of a point, say $(2, 3)$, by starting on the x-axis
at the value of the first number, in this case 2. From there, move
up by the value of the second number, in this case 3.

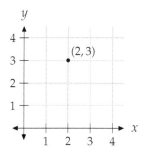

Make shapes for fun A fun activity is to create a connect-the-dots
puzzle with a list of ordered pairs. You create a list of points
that your child plots and connects together. If your child plots
all of the points correctly, the points connect to form a picture of
a kite, sailboat, or some other drawing.

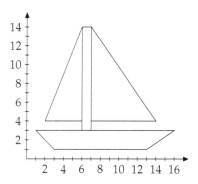

Add a twist to this by making some of the coordinate values
be things to calculate or puzzle out. For example, make points
such as $(2 \times 3, 1)$ or $(3^2 - 4, 8 \div 4 + 1)$.

Reverse this activity by having your child create a picture and
giving you a list of points to plot.

6.9 Transformations

Learning about transformations of the plane.

 Transformations A *transformation* is a rule for moving points around in a plane. The location where a point is sent by a transformation is called the point's *image*.

Rigid motions A *rigid motion*, also called an *isometry*, is a transformation that maintains the distance between every pair of points. Rigid motions also maintain all angles. Because rigid motions maintain distances and angles, they move figures to new figures which are congruent to the original.

There are three basic kinds of rigid motions.

Translation A *translation*, which is also called a *glide transformation*, moves all points a fixed distance in a fixed direction. It is as though the plane is given a simple push in a direction.

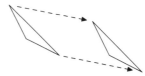

Reflection A *reflection* about a line moves each point directly across the line to the same distance on the other side.

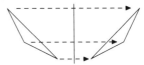

Rotation A *rotation* about a point spins the whole plane a specified number of degrees about the point.

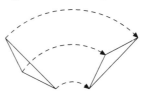

Dilations A *dilation* moves every point by a scaling factor farther or closer to a given fixed point. If the scaling factor is bigger than 1, it is called an *expansion*, and if it is less than 1, it is called a *contraction*.

Dilations maintain the shape of every figure, but change the size by the scaling factor. Because of this, dilations send the points of a figure to a new figure that is similar to the original.

Composition Use two transformations to create a new transformation by moving points using the first transformation, and then moving points again using the second transformation. This is called *composition*.

For example, suppose one transformation moves points 2 spaces to the right, and the second moves points 3 spaces up. Composing these two transformations will move a point 2 spaces to the right, and then move it 3 spaces up.

Every rigid motion can be created by composing a combination of translations, reflections, and rotations.

One interesting experiment to do with your child is to see what happens when two reflections are composed. It turns out that composing two reflections produces a translation if the lines are parallel, or a rotation about the intersection point if the lines intersect. A consequence of this experiment is that every rigid motion can be achieved by composing a sequence of reflections.

Transformations in art Many of the drawings of M. C. Escher have patterns produced by translations, reflections, and rotations. Look at one of his drawings and discuss which transformations are present. Have your child make Escher-style drawings by starting with a single sketch of an animal or object, and then duplicate that sketch around the drawing by repeatedly using one or more kinds of transformations.

6.10 Symmetry

 LESSON | Learning about symmetry in shapes.

Practice ▷   Similarity and congruence give you some ways to talk with your child about how figures are the same or how they differ. Symmetry gives you a way to describe how parts of a shape are the same or different from other parts.

There are two kinds of symmetry I will be looking at—symmetry about a line and rotational symmetry.

Symmetry about a line If the figure on one side of a line is the mirror image of the figure on the other side, then the line is called a *line of symmetry* for the figure. Using the language of transformations, the reflection of the figure about that line takes the figure to itself. A figure which has a line of symmetry is said to be *symmetric* about that line.

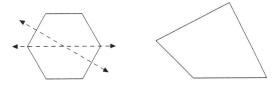

The shape on the left has many lines of symmetry, two of which are drawn in. The second figure does not have any lines of symmetry.

Have your child look for symmetry in all sorts of things. Many things in nature have lines of symmetry. For example, most leaves are symmetric about their center line, and so are most animals.

Flags are another fun source of symmetry. Children usually enjoy looking up the flags of countries, and most flags have lines of symmetry.

One way to have your child check a figure for a line of symmetry is to copy the figure to a piece of paper. If your child folds the paper along the line and the two halves of the figure match, then it is a line of symmetry.

Another way to check is to use a small hand mirror with a flat edge. Place the edge of the mirror across the figure and look at the remaining partial figure together with its reflection in the mirror. The edge of the mirror forms a line of symmetry for the new figure produced from the partial original figure and its reflection. If this new figure is identical to the original figure, then this is a line of symmetry for the original figure.

Rotational symmetry A figure has *rotational symmetry* about a point if some rotation produces a new figure that is identical to the original. For example, a starfish has rotational symmetry about its center for rotations of 72 degrees, 144 degrees, 216 degrees, and 288 degrees—these are the multiples of $72 = 360 \div 5$.

A special kind of rotational symmetry occurs when the rotation is 180 degrees. In this case the symmetry is called a *point symmetry*.

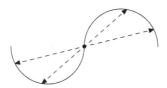

6.11 Polygons

LESSON Learning about polygons and some of their properties.

 Practice The best way to practice this is to make a habit of using these names when talking about everyday things with your child.

Polygon A *polygon* is a closed plane figure made up of line segments joined only at their endpoints. Each line segment is called a *side*, and each endpoint is called a *vertex*. Polygons are named after the number of sides they have.

Number of Sides	Name of Polygon
3	Triangle
4	Quadrilateral
5	Pentagon
6	Hexagon
8	Octagon

A *regular polygon* is one in which all of the sides have the same length, and all of the angles have the same measure.

pentagon   regular hexagon   regular octagon

Polygons are all around us, so there are lots of opportunities to use this vocabulary. Street signs give some examples. Yield signs are triangles, speed limit signs are rectangles, and stop signs are octagons.

Building features have lots of polygons. Doors and windows are usually rectangles, floor tiles are sometimes hexagons, and there are many triangles in most bridges.

Diagonals A diagonal of a polygon is a line segment, that is not a side, that connects two vertices. The quadrilateral below has the diagonals from A to C and B to D drawn in.

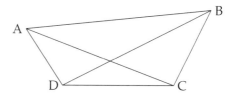

Interior and exterior angles At each vertex of a polygon, there is a supplementary pair of angles formed by the crossing sides (if you think of the sides extended to be lines). Of the pair, the angle on the inside of the polygon is the *interior angle*, and its supplement is the *exterior angle*.

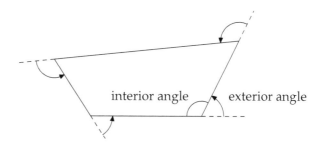

interior angle   exterior angle

Have your child verify that exterior angles add up to 360 degrees by drawing a large polygon using chalk on a large open area. Mark one vertex to start and end at. Have your child walk along each side and then make a partial turn at each vertex to look in the direction of the next side. After walking all the way around the polygon and pointing again in the original direction, your child will have made one complete 360 degree rotation.

The exterior and interior angles are supplementary, so each pair of them adds up to 180°. For an n-sided polygon this gives:

$$n \times 180° = \text{sum of both angles at each vertex}$$
$$= \text{sum of exterior angles} + \text{sum of interior angles}$$
$$= 360° + \text{sum of interior angles}$$

So, the sum of the interior angles is $n180° - 360° = (n - 2)180°$.

> **RULE** For an n-sided polygon:
> 1. The sum of the exterior angles is $360°$.
> 2. The sum of the interior angles is $(n-2)180°$.

Verify this formula for interior angles with your child. Do this by drawing any triangle or quadrilateral on a piece of paper. Cut out the figure, tear off the three or four corners, and then place the corners with sides touching and all of the vertices next to each other. The three angles for a triangle will fit together to make a straight $180°$ line, and the four angles for a quadrilateral will go all the way around to make $360°$.

Perimeter The sum of the lengths of the sides of a polygon is called its *perimeter*. For a regular n-sided polygon, the perimeter is n times the length of one of its sides.

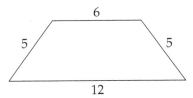

For this trapezoid, the perimeter is $6 + 5 + 12 + 5 = 28$.

6.12 Triangles

LESSON   Learning the names of different kinds of triangles.

Practice ▶   **Interior angles** In Section 6.11: *Polygons* I showed that the sum of the interior angles of a triangle is 180 degrees. Because of this a triangle can have at most one angle that is 90 degrees or more.

Names using angles Some triangle names are based on the largest angle of the triangle.

Obtuse triangle One angle is larger than 90 degrees.

Right triangle One angle is 90 degrees. The side opposite the right angle is called the *hypotenuse,* and the other two sides are called *legs.*

Acute triangle All angles are less than 90 degrees.

Equiangular triangle All angles are 60 degrees. Because it is also true that all of the sides are equal, these triangles are also called equilateral. The name equilateral is used more commonly than equiangular.

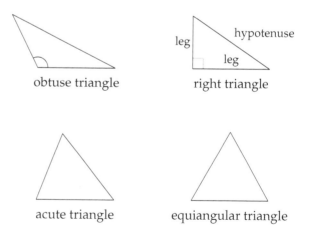

obtuse triangle   right triangle

acute triangle   equiangular triangle

Names using sides Some names for triangles are based on the number of equal sides.

> **Scalene triangle** All of the sides of the triangle have different lengths.

> **Isosceles triangle** Two of the sides are the same. In an isosceles triangle it is also true that two of the angles are equal.

> **Equilateral triangle** All of the sides are the same. Because it is also true that all of the angles are equal, these triangles are also called equiangular.

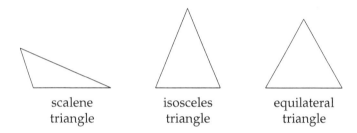

| scalene triangle | isosceles triangle | equilateral triangle |

Vocabulary games There is a lot of vocabulary here. Make learning the terminology more fun by playing scavenger hunt or Concentration games, as described in the introduction to the chapter.

6.13   Triangle Inequality

Learning about the triangle inequality.

 Practice ▶   We have all heard the phrase "the shortest distance between two points is a straight line." Here is a theorem that says much the same thing.

> **RULE**   **Triangle Inequality:** The sum of the lengths of two sides of a triangle is greater than the length of the remaining side.

Practice this idea with your child by giving the lengths of two sides of a triangle, and asking what is possible for the length of the third side.

For example, suppose the lengths of the two sides are 4 and 7. Cut two lengths of string to be 4 inches and 7 inches. Fix both ends of the longer 7-inch string to pins on a board, and pin one end of the shorter 4-inch string to one end of the 7-inch string.

Show the whole circle of possibilities for the 4-inch side by swinging it in an arc from the pinned end. Your child will see that the longest the third side can be is $4 + 7 = 11$ inches, and the shortest is $7 - 4 = 3$ inches.

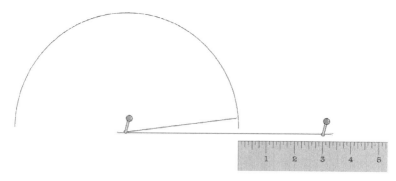

6.14 Quadrilaterals

 LESSON Learning names of different kinds of quadrilaterals.

Practice▷

In Section 6.11: *Polygons* I showed that the sum of the interior angles of a quadrilateral is 360 degrees. An easy way to remember this is that a rectangle has four 90 degree angles.

Quadrilaterals are named after the characteristics of their side lengths, angle sizes, and whether they have parallel sides.

Trapezoid These have exactly one pair of parallel sides.

Kite These often look like kites. They have two pairs of adjacent sides of equal lengths. The diagonals of a kite are perpendicular, and one diagonal bisects the other.

Parallelogram These have two pairs of parallel sides. In parallelograms, opposite sides and opposite angles have equal size. Also, the diagonals bisect each other.

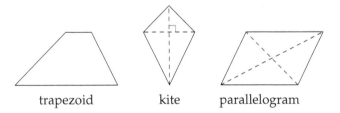

trapezoid   kite   parallelogram

Rhombus All four sides have equal lengths. Every rhombus is a parallelogram. The diagonals in a rhombus are perpendicular and they bisect each other.

Rectangle All four angles are equal, and are therefore 90 degrees. Every rectangle is a parallelogram. The diagonals have equal length and bisect each other.

Square All four sides and all four angles are equal. Every square is a rectangle and a rhombus. The diagonals are equal and are perpendicular bisectors of each other.

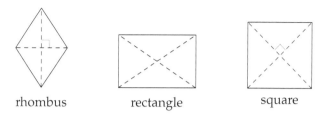

| rhombus | rectangle | square |

Relationships Along with learning the descriptions and characteristics, your child should learn how the various types are related. For example, all squares are rectangles, but not all rectangles are squares. Your child should be able to give an example of a rectangle that is not a square.

Here is a chart showing which types are subtypes of others. For example, rhombus is connected beneath parallelogram, because every rhombus is a parallelogram.

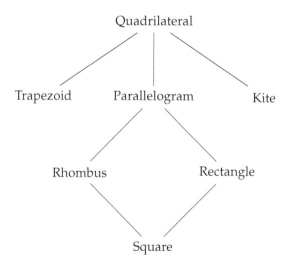

Vocabulary games This is another big bunch of words for your child to learn. One way to make learning the terminology more fun is by playing scavenger hunt or Concentration games. These are both described in the introduction to the chapter.

6.15 Circles

 LESSON | Learning the characteristics of circles. |

Practice ▷   The best way to practice this is to make a habit of using these terms with your child. There are lots of examples of circles in your child's world—wheels on a car or bike, the outline of the moon, sun, or a ball. Wall clocks are circles, and the minute and second hands are very close to being radii.

Circle A *circle* is the set of points in a plane that are a given distance from a point called the *center*. The center is not considered to be part of the circle.

Chord A line segment that starts and stops on the circle is called a *chord*.

Diameter A chord that goes through the center is called a *diameter*.

Radius A line segment that has one endpoint at the center and the other on the circle is called a *radius*.

Arc A continuous section along the circle is called an *arc*.

    The length of a diameter is also called the *diameter*, and the length of a radius is also called the *radius*. These double meanings do not usually cause any confusion.

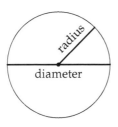

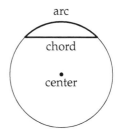

Pi and circumference The *circumference* of a circle is the length going once around the circle.

All circles have the same shape, so they are all similar. Because of this, the ratio of the circumference to the diameter is constant. 18th century European mathematicians named this important ratio after the Greek letter π (often written as "pi"), which is pronounced "pie" by westerners and "pea" by Greeks.

> **RULE** $\pi = \text{pi} = \frac{\text{circumference}}{\text{diameter}} \sim 3.14159$

It is important to realize that this is just the definition of the value of pi. It is not some sort of magical relationship that just happens to equal pi.

The way this relationship is usually written is in the formula for the circumference. In this formula d stands for the diameter, r stands for the radius, and C stands for the circumference.

> **RULE** $C = \pi d = 2\pi r$

Approximating π Your child can investigate the value of π. Fix one end of a long string and draw a circle using the string—perhaps with chalk on cement.

Use string to find out what the circumference of the circle is. Divide the length of the circumference by the length of the radius, and that should be close to 2π. You will probably need to help with the division and make the result into a fraction.

A similar experiment is to use a roll of tape or ribbon. Measure the length of one wind of tape or ribbon, and divide that by the diameter of the spool. This should be close to the value of π.

There are two standard approximations for the value of π. The usual one is $\frac{22}{7} = 3\frac{1}{7}$, which is accurate to 2 decimal places. An even better value is obtained by taking the sequence 113355, splitting it in half, and making a fraction. The value $\frac{355}{113}$ is accurate to 6 decimal places!

A fun experiment to do with your child is to look at lengths involving a tennis ball can holding three balls. Ask your child which length is longer, the height of the can or going once around the can. Most children will say the height is the longer length. Confirm that the two lengths are nearly equal using a piece of string. You can then talk about the formulas, that the circumference is π times the diameter of a tennis ball, and the height of the can is a little more than 3 times the diameter.

Tangent lines and circles A line that touches a circle at exactly one point is said to be *tangent* to it. A tangent line is perpendicular to the radius that ends at the point of tangency.

Two circles are said to be *tangent* to each other if they share a single point. Notice in the diagram that there are two ways for two circles to be tangent.

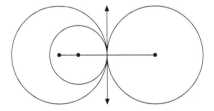

In this diagram the circles share a common tangent line at the point of tangency. Since the radii are all perpendicular to the tangent line at the same point, the radii and the centers all lie on the same line, that is, they are collinear.

6.16   Straight-edge and compass

 LESSON | Learning to do constructions using straight-edge and compass.

Practice⟶ **Constructions** These constructions provide a physical way to create geometric shapes and work with geometric ideas. They involve using a straight-edge to make straight lines, and a compass to measure lengths and sweep out circles. For young children, buy a compass that does not have any sharp ends.

GeoGebra **and** *Geometer's Sketchpad* The software programs *GeoGebra* and *Geometer's Sketchpad* are fabulous programs based on straight-edge and compass constructions. They are very similar, but *GeoGebra* is free and easy to use from a web browser, which makes it the more natural choice to use.

These programs are great for a child that has limitations that may make these constructions frustrating. They are also very dynamic, so it makes it easy to try things out. For example, after making a series of constructions, move a point around and see how the diagram changes without having to redraw anything.

Make geometric diagrams In addition to making the constructions listed in this section, challenge your child to make artistic pictures using these tools. Beautiful pictures can be made using different colors in regions created by overlapping circles, arcs, and lines meeting at 30, 45, 60, and 90 degrees.

A few sample constructions The following are just a quick sampling of constructions that can be made using a straight-edge and compass. They illustrate how these drawing tools can be used to explore some of the deeper geometric relationships. If your child is interested, you can find quite a few more such constructions on the internet by using the search string *straight-edge and compass* in a search engine.

Perpendicular bisector for a segment The *perpendicular bisector* for a line segment is the line that bisects the segment and is perpendicular to it. To create the perpendicular bisector, set the compass to any distance greater than half the length of the segment. (1) Sweep out circles from both ends of the segment. (2) Draw a line through the two points where the circles meet.

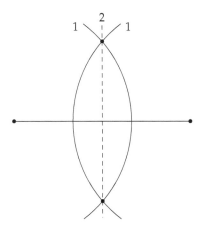

The construction of the perpendicular bisector works because of the following rule.

> **RULE** **Perpendicular Bisector:** The perpendicular bisector of a line segment is exactly made up of the points that are equidistant from the two endpoints.

I will use the perpendicular bisector construction in the next two constructions. The first construction gives a method for finding the center of a circle, and the second describes a process for finding a circle that goes through the three corners of a triangle.

Find the center of a circle (1) Use the straight edge to create two chords on the circle. Any two chords will work, as long as they are not parallel. (2) Construct the perpendicular bisectors for the two chords.

The point of intersection of these bisectors is the center. This works because the center is equidistant from all points on the circle. In particular, the center is equidistant from the two endpoints of each of the chords.

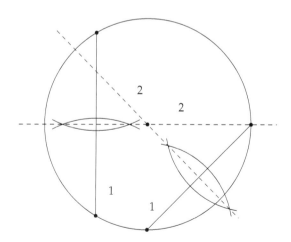

Circumscribe a circle about a triangle A circle is said to circumscribe a triangle ABC if it intersects the triangle at the three points—*A*, *B*, and *C*. Since the desired circle has the sides of the triangle as chords, we can use the previous method for constructing the center of a circle. Start by constructing the perpendicular bisectors of $\overline{AC}$ and $\overline{CB}$, and then use the intersection of those bisectors as the center of the circle.

(1) Use the compass to draw three circles the same size that are centered at *A*, *B*, and *C*. Choose a large enough radius for the circles so that they will intersect. (2) Use the straight-edge to draw the perpendicular bisectors through the pairs of points of intersection. (3) Draw the center where the two perpendicular bisectors meet. (4) Use the compass to draw a circle centered at the point from step 3 and going through the corners of the triangle.

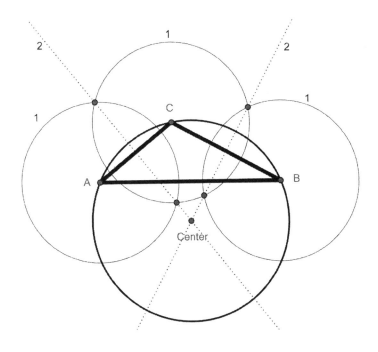

6.17   Areas

Learning area formulas for triangles, quadrilaterals, and circles.

RELATED

You may want to cover some of the material in Section 7.2: *Area* in the *Measurements* Chapter at the same time that you do this section.

Practice ▷

Unit square The starting point for understanding area is the unit square. Area is described in square units. For example, a square 1″ by 1″ has an area of 1 square inch. This is a definition; it is not something to be figured out.

Rectangle Find the area of a rectangle by calculating how many unit squares will fit in it. Do several examples with your child until the pattern is clear.

For example, in a 2 by 4 rectangle there are 2 rows with 4 unit squares in each row. This gives a total of $2 \times 4 = 8$ unit squares.

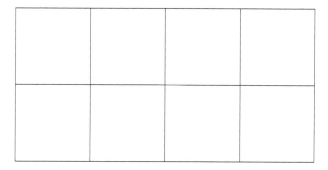

After experimentation, your child will see that the area in general is the width times the length.

RULE   Rectangle Area = Width × Length

You can also describe this as the base times the height, which is the description used for parallelograms.

Parallelogram There are two ways to demonstrate the area formula for parallelograms to your child.

> **RULE** Parallelogram Area = Base × Height

One way is to cut off a right trianglular corner of the parallelogram, and paste it on the opposite side. This creates a rectangle with the same area, as shown in the illustration.

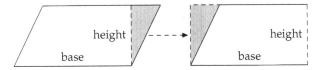

Another way is to use a side view of a deck of cards (or a ream of paper). Show your child that the area of the side of the deck does not change when you slide the cards over. No matter how you slide them, the edges of the cards make up the slices of the area of the side, and those edges add up to the same total area.

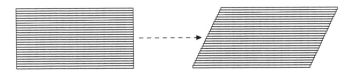

Triangle Start by working with right triangles. Draw in the full rectangle that has this triangle as one half of it. From the drawing, the area is half of the product of the legs of the triangle.

> **RULE** Triangle Area = $\frac{1}{2}$ × Base × Height

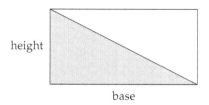

base

Find the area of any triangle using the same method used for parallelograms. Take one side of the triangle for the base, and draw a parallel line through the opposite vertex. The original triangle will have the same area as a right triangle with the same base and height. The areas are the same because the cross sections are the same.

Trapezoid Find the area of a trapezoid by using one of the diagonals to cut up the trapezoid into two triangles, and then add up the areas of those triangles. However, in my experience, children usually do not gain any insight from that derivation, so I generally just give them the area formula and leave it at that.

RULE Trapezoid Area $= \frac{1}{2} \times \text{Height} \times (\text{Base1} + \text{Base2})$

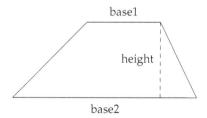

Circle The area of a circle comes from the circumference formula $C = 2\pi r$. Break up a circle into little triangles that have one vertex in the center, and the other two vertices on the edge of the circle.

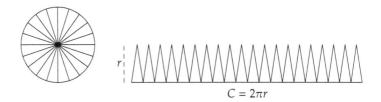

$$C = 2\pi r$$

Cheat just a little by unrolling the sliced up circle to be a row of triangles. The total area of these triangles is half of the height, which is r, times the total length, which is the circumference.

$$\text{Area} = \frac{1}{2}rC = \frac{1}{2}r(2\pi r) = \pi r^2$$

RULE   Circle Area = πr^2

Maximum area One interesting investigation with areas is to find which shapes have the largest area for a given perimeter.

For example, ask your child to find the area of a few rectangles that have the same perimeter. Your child will discover that the square has the greatest area.

Although it is not very easy to do, your child may also discover or be convinced that, for a given perimeter, a regular triangle is worse than a regular quadrilateral, which is worse than a regular pentagon, and so on. Finally, the most efficient figure of all is the circle.

6.18   Pythagorean Theorem

 | Learning about the Pythagorean Theorem.

Practice ▷ **The theorem** This is one of the most famous theorems in mathematics. It is named after Pythagoras, a Greek mathematician who lived in the 6th century B.C. Although he may have been the first to prove the relationship, there is evidence that people knew of it at least a thousand years before him.

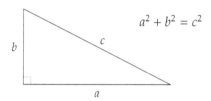

> **RULE   Pythagorean Theorem:**   The sum of the squares of the legs of a right triangle is equal to the square of the hypotenuse. In terms of the diagram above, $a^2 + b^2 = c^2$.

Triples There are an infinite number of what are called *Pythagorean triples*. These triples are made up of three whole numbers that satisfy the equation $a^2 + b^2 = c^2$.

Children often have a lot of fun discovering Pythagorean triples. The most well known triple is $3^2 + 4^2 = 5^2$. Using similar triangles, any multiple of $(3, 4, 5)$ will also work. For example, $(6, 8, 10)$ and $(9, 12, 15)$ are also Pythagorean triples.

There are also a lot of triples that do not come from triangles similar to $(3, 4, 5)$. For example, $(5, 12, 13)$ and $(7, 24, 25)$ come from triangles that are not similar to $(3, 4, 5)$.

Construction There is evidence that the triple $(3, 4, 5)$ was used by builders in ancient Egypt to make sure that an angle was a right angle.

Carpenters still use this today. Suppose you have laid out a wall, and you want to make sure the wall was built squarely with right angles. Measure 3 feet along one board, mark the spot, then measure 4 feet along the other board, and mark that spot. If the distance between the two spots is exactly 5 feet, then you have a right angle. If it is less than 5 feet, the angle is too small, and if it is greater than 5 feet, the angle is too big.

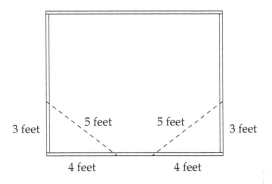

Square roots When looking for triples, you have a choice to make. Either teach your child about square roots, or make sure that all of your examples work out evenly. This book does not cover square roots, but don't let that stop you if your child is interested in it.

The Greeks during the time of Pythagoras were quite disturbed that the length of the diagonal of a unit square is $\sqrt{2}$. They had thought that all lengths that occurred in nature were ratios of whole numbers. When they discovered that $\sqrt{2}$ cannot be represented as a fraction it upset many of those ideas.

6.19 Three-dimensional shapes

Playing with 3-dimensional shapes.

Practice➤ These are some important three-dimensional shapes your child should learn. Some of these shapes will show up in the block sets your child plays with, so that will be one arena where you can discuss them.

Prisms The horizontal cross-sections of these shapes are congruent from bottom to top.

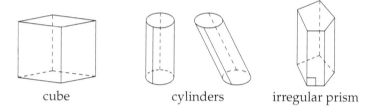

cube   cylinders   irregular prism

Pyramids and cones The horizontal cross-sections of these shapes are similar from bottom to top.

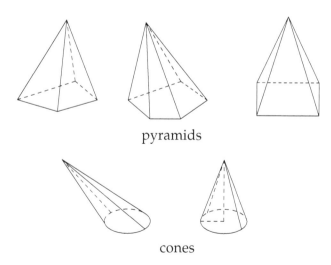

pyramids

cones

Platonic solids There are five special solid figures that are named after Plato, the Greek mathematician and philosopher. In such a solid, each side is the same regular polygon, and each corner has the same number of polygons coming into it.

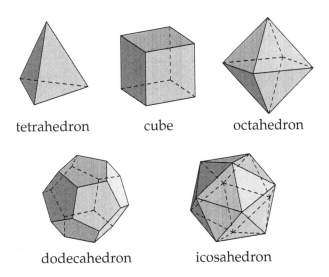

tetrahedron   cube   octahedron

dodecahedron   icosahedron

Spheres These are ball-like shapes. Geodesic domes often look like hemispheres.

Kits There are several kits on the market that simplify making three-dimensional shapes. One of my favorites is Klikko, made by Kydko International. Here are some shapes made using this kit.

There are some other good kits listed in Section 9.7: *3-dimensional construction kits* in the *Manipulatives* Chapter.

Another good source of three-dimensional models is to make them out of paper using patterns. There are books that have these patterns drawn on stiff paper ready to cut out and glue. You can also find the patterns in books or on the web, and sketch them on stiff paper yourself.

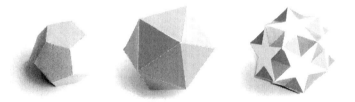

You can also make three-dimensional figures using simple materials around the house. For example, make models using spaghetti, toothpicks, or straws joined together using marshmallow pieces or gum drops.

Making toy models Constructing any three-dimensional toy model will teach your child about shapes and relationships. The model does not need to be geometric—any model, whether of a plane, a car, or something else, works equally well.

6.20 Volumes and surface areas

RELATED

Another way to measure volumes is to use liquid measures. You may want to cover some of the material in Section 7.3: *Volume* in the *Measurements* Chapter at the same time that you do this section.

Practice ▷

Stay with boxes and prisms when first playing with these ideas— leave the more complicated shapes and formulas for much later, after your child is comfortable with the concepts.

The majority of these formulas can be explained and demonstrated with shapes you have around the house. However, some of these formulas end up being magic. For example, the $\frac{1}{3}$ that enters the formulas for the volumes of pyramids and cones is only explainable using mathematics way beyond the scope of this book.

Unit cube This is where the understanding of volume begins. The volume of a cube that is 1″ by 1″ by 1″ is 1 cubic inch. This is a definition; it is not something to be figured out.

Box Volume is calculated by finding the number of unit cubes that will fit into a shape. For boxes with whole number lengths, this is easy and is the place to start.

For example, look at how many cubic inches will fit into a box that is 4″ by 5″ by 3″ tall. The 4″ by 5″ bottom has room for 20 square inches, that is, the faces for 20 of the 1″ cubes. The 1″ cubes can be stacked 3 high in this space. So, this gives $3 \times 4 \times 5 = 60$ cubic inches.

> **RULE** Box Volume = Height × Width × Length

The surface area of a box is the sum of the areas of its six rectangular faces. It is a good place to start practicing surface areas, but no special formula is needed.

Prisms Boxes are a special case of prisms, which are the next shape to look at.

All of the horizontal cross-sections of a prism are congruent to its bottom or top. A point on the edge of the base can be traced in a straight line along the side of the solid to the corresponding point on the edge of the top. Boxes and cylinders are examples of prisms.

RULE Prism Volume = Height × (Area of base)

The surface area of a prism is the area of the top and bottom, together with the area of the sides. The area of the side of a prism is sometimes referred to as its *lateral area*.

If you think of spreading out, or unrolling, the side of a prism, you can make it into one rectangle. For prisms that are cylinders, this is like the label on a soup can. One of the dimensions of this rectangle is the height of the prism, and the other is the length of the outside of the base.

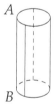 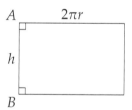

The length of the outside of the base is its perimeter, which can also be called the circumference if the base is a circle. In either case, this gives a lateral area of:

Height × (Perimeter of base)

RULE Prism Surface Area
= 2 × (Area of base)
+ Height × (Perimeter of base)

Pyramid and cone All of the cross-sections of these shapes are similar to the base. The surface area formula is a bit beyond the level of this book, so I will just provide the formula for the volume.

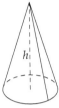

> **RULE** Pyramid or Cone Volume
> $= \frac{1}{3} \times$ Height $\times$ (Area of base)

Notice that this volume formula is almost exactly the same as the volume formula for a prism—the only difference is the introduction of the magic $\frac{1}{3}$ factor.

Sphere Similar to my treatment of pyramids and cones, I will just be covering the volume formula for a sphere. Let r be the radius of the sphere.

> **RULE** Sphere Volume $= \frac{4}{3}\pi r^3$

6.21 Graph theory

 LESSON | Learning how to use graphs to solve puzzles.

Practice ▶ The term graph often refers to plotting points in a coordinate system. This section is not about that kind of graph.

The graphs looked at in this section are described as a collection of nodes (points) that have connections between some pairs of them.

Here are three puzzles. Next to the first two puzzles is a drawing of a graph that will be used to work on the puzzle. After the three puzzles are described, I will talk about how to solve them.

Bridges of Konigsburg This is a famous problem attributed to the mathematician Euler. The town of Konigsburg was located where two rivers come together, and there was an island in the middle. There were seven bridges as shown in the map. The story goes that one year the town decided they wanted to have a parade that would cross each of the bridges exactly once. Which path should they follow, if they could do it at all?

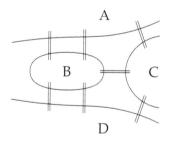 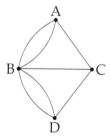

The graph is obtained by using one node for each region of land. Place a connection between each pair of nodes for each bridge.

Side crossings Consider the following diagram of rectangles. Can you draw a single, unbroken path that crosses each side in the diagram exactly once? You are not allowed to cross corners or travel along the sides.

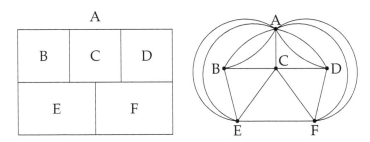

As with the first problem, make a graph where the nodes are the separate regions. This time there will be one connection for each side between two regions.

Mail delivery problem A letter carrier is to drop off the mail along the streets in a town. He wants to visit each street exactly once. Which path should he follow for each of these diagrams? How does the problem change if he wants to start and end at the same place? Here are a few such layouts, but you can make more of your own very easily.

These three problems start off sounding different, but they can be translated into the same type of graph problem. The problem for each graph is: Is it possible to travel the entire graph by traversing each connection exactly once? A second question is whether this can be done by starting and ending at the same node.

This is a perfect opportunity to teach your child a basic lesson in problem solving.

> **RULE** If you are having trouble solving a complex problem, try solving several simpler versions of the problem. Look for patterns in these simpler solutions that will be useful in solving the harder problem.

Start off by looking at several smaller graphs and see what happens for these. If your child does not discover the pattern, provide some help. Look at what happens when a node has an even or odd number of connections. The key observation is that nodes with an odd number of connections must be the starting or ending node of a path through the graph. The first two problems of this section cannot be solved because they have more than two nodes with an odd number of connections.

There are lots of other interesting questions in graph theory. For example, another question is what might be called the delivery person problem. Is it possible to travel through a graph visiting each node exactly once (dropping off a package at each node)?

CHAPTER 7

Measurements

Making measurements builds up a sense of quantity and size, and provides practice with comparing lengths, weights, or volumes of two or more objects. By understanding how 26 inches compares with 25 inches and 28 inches, a child also learns how the number 26 compares with 25 and 28. This also develops skill with the taking of measurements with different instruments, and gives practice assessing characteristics of objects in terms of standard units.

There are many different features of a thing that may be measured. Some of the aspects we can measure are its length, area, volume, weight, and temperature. Each of these is measured in terms of some kinds of units. For example, length can be measured in inches, feet, centimeters, meters, miles, kilometers, and many other less common units.

The age and ability of your child will greatly influence how sophisticated the measurement exercises should be. Practice the English measurements (e.g. feet and inches) as well as the metric ones (e.g. meters and centimeters).

In addition to knowing the two standard measurement systems, your child should be comfortable converting between any two units measuring the same aspect of a thing. For example, your child should know how to convert between units such as feet, meters, miles, and kilometers.

Having an intuitive feeling for the size of things is just as important as being able to make precise mathematical calculations. For example, your child should learn that a meter is just over a yard, a liter is about the same as a quart, and a kilometer is about $\frac{3}{5}$ of a mile.

As your child becomes familiar with taking measurements, ask which unit is appropriate for measuring a certain object. For example, you might ask "Shall we use inches, feet, or miles for measuring how far we are going to drive to Grandma's house?", or "Shall we use inches or feet for measuring the length of this pencil?"

Along these same lines, have your child practice estimating what a measurement will be before doing it. Make a game of seeing who can make the closer estimate before a measurement is taken.

As your child gains familiarity with the names of the various units, use abbreviations for the units from time to time. For example, instead of always writing 4 feet, write 4 ft. or 4' sometimes.

Time is another property to be measured and calculated. In the first book I covered clock reading and basic calendar information. In this book I discuss the various units of time, calculating durations, and working with time zones.

The basic properties of length, area, volume, weight, temperature, and time can be mixed together in a great variety of ways. This falls under the general heading of rates. For example, speed is length per time, and density is weight per volume. Increasingly, your child will be experiencing rates and needing to calculate with them.

A note for the technically oriented. There is a difference between weight and mass, but I will not be concerned with that difference in this book.

During this time your child will be developing skills in doing arithmetic with measurements. Some of this arithmetic, such as adding 23 meters to 46 meters, is straightforward. But other calculations require some training and practice.

Adding or subtracting 4'8" and 2'9" requires regrouping in a new way. This new kind of regrouping will give your child a fresh perspective on the regrouping done for addition and subtraction of multi-digit numbers. Also, dividing 2 hours, 25 minutes, and 41 seconds by 5, to find an average time, involves the recognition that the various units need to be converted to a single common unit.

The material in this chapter combines well with several other topics in this book. For example, when recording daily measurements of something like temperature, your child can practice graphing and statistical work. Your child can practice looking for patterns and relationships in data. For example, recording elevation, temperature, and pressure as you travel into some mountains, or perhaps recording miles per gallon as you take a road trip that involves city travel and highway travel.

Making and recording measurements, looking for patterns, creating models and explanations for the data, is the beginning of science for your child. There is a wonderful world of observations and ideas to explore and play with together.

7.1 Length

 Learning how to measure and describe lengths.

Practice ▷ **Measure everything** Your main tools for measuring length will be a ruler or tape measure. Measure all sorts of things, such as erasers, pencils, fingers, arms, people, walls, and so on.

A fun project is to make a diagram of a room, backyard, or even a floor plan for your house. A more difficult project is to make a map involving the location of your house together with some other important places around town. These projects give excellent practice with measurements, scaling factors, and geometry. Make the measurements as precise or approximate as is appropriate for the skill level of your child.

English or Metric Stick with one or the other of these for the first few months or so. Eventually, introduce your child to the other system. If you are measuring feet and inches, reinforce the values of the fractions for halves, fourths, and eighths. If you are measuring meters and centimeters, reinforce tenths.

Pacing A good way to start measuring longer distances is to have your child pace out the distance and count the number of steps taken. In this way you can compare the length of a room in your house with the length of your driveway. You can find out which rooms in your house are the widest or the narrowest.

Car trips Around this time, get your child used to understanding the distances for miles or kilometers. Use your car to measure the distance for typical car, walking, or biking trips you like to take, and then talk about those distances on your travels. If it's a mile to your favorite park or playground, then compare that to the three mile trip to the store, or the 50 mile trip to a close relative, or the 2,000 mile trip to a more distant relative or friend.

Where the names come from You may enjoy exploring looking up the backgrounds of many of the measurement words with your child. Here are some brief descriptions.

Inch This comes from the Latin "uncia," meaning a twelfth part of a unit.

Foot This, pretty obviously, comes originally from the length of a person's foot. Feet are different from person to person, and they have also changed over the years. Your child may enjoy checking to see whose feet are closest to being a foot in length.

Yard This word comes from root words meaning a stick or rod. It was originally meant to be one stride in length.

Mile There are many lengths for a mile. Many countries have their own definitions of a mile. There is also a Nautical mile. The American mile seems to come from a Roman mile, which was a thousand paces. The word mile comes from "mille" meaning one thousand. A pace is two steps, which is typically a bit less than 2 yards.

Meter This was originally intended to be one ten millionth of the distance from the North Pole to the equator, going along the surface of the earth. It is very close to this distance.

7.2 Area

 Learning how to measure and describe areas.

Practice▷ **Square units** Area is measured in the same way as all other measurements. A standard unit is used, and then the object is measured in terms of how many units are needed to fill it. For area, the unit is square inches, square centimeters, square feet, square meters, or the square of some other length.

1″

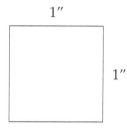

1″

For example, show your child that 1 square inch is a square that is 1 inch on a side. Just as you measure the length of something in inches by seeing how many inches fit in its length, so you measure the area of something by seeing how many square inches are needed to fill it up.

Measuring geometric shapes Follow along the discussion of areas in Section 6.17: *Areas* in the *Geometry* Chapter. Start with rectangular areas and convince your child of the following rule.

RULE The area of a rectangle is the width times the length.

Continue with the material in Section 6.17: *Areas* to obtain formulas for the areas of parallelograms, triangles, and circles. Apply these formulas by measuring shapes of objects around your home or playground. For example, for circles you can find the area of plates, bicycle wheels, and car tires.

Approximating irregular shapes This step is very important for ce-
menting the idea that measuring area is a matter of counting up
square inches (or whatever unit you are using). In the absence
of doing this step, it is very tempting to think of measuring area
as being the same as applying a formula and multiplying width
times length, and lose sight of what is really going on. Most
high school math students I have asked about area say "width
times length"—they have no other relationship to the idea.

Take any shape you wish to find the area of. The outline of
your child's shoe can be fun. Now draw an inch grid across the
region of the shape. Finally, using whatever fraction your child
is comfortable with (say fourths or tenths), count up the number
of square inches and approximate partial square inches inside
the shape—this total is close to the area of the shape.

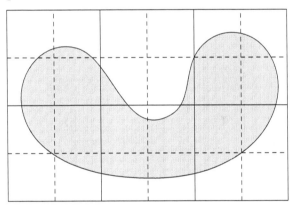

Experiment with different size grids ($\frac{1}{2}''$ in this case) to see what
effect that has on the accuracy of your approximations of the
area.

Instead of drawing a grid on top of your figure, draw the figure
on graph paper that has convenient distances between lines.
For example, if the grid lines are $\frac{1}{4}''$ apart, then each square will
represent $\frac{1}{16}$ square inch.

7.3 Volume

LESSON | Learning how to measure and describe volumes.

Practice▷ **Kitchen measurements** Liquid measurements are great for letting a child play with comparing and adjusting sizes. Practice by having your child help measure things in the kitchen.

Practice the whole range of measurements, from teaspoons, tablespoons, and cups, up through pints, quarts, and gallons—or if you are doing metric measurements, milliliters up through liters. Measuring items for cooking recipes is also a great opportunity for basic practicing with fractions.

Cup sets In some educational supply stores you can buy sets of cups that have volumes marked from 1 to 10. For example, Discovery Toys sells a set of cups called Measure Up!® Cups. With these cups your child can see, feel, and compare just how big each size is. Your child can pour a filled 5-cup into a 7-cup, and confirm that there is room for a filled 2-cup.

You can pose some sophisticated puzzles with these cups. Ask questions such as "if you have only a 5- and a 7- cup, how can you end up with exactly 2 (or harder, 3) units in one of the cups?"

Displacement An excellent way to measure the volume of an odd shaped object that is water-tight is to measure its displacement in a tub of water. For this, it is helpful to know that one US liquid ounce is about $1\frac{4}{5}$ cubic inches, and one milliliter is one cubic centimeter and about $\frac{6}{100}$ cubic inches.

For example, find the volume of a light bulb this way. Take a large measuring cup and put in enough water so that the water will cover the light bulb when it is put in. Record the measure of the water without the light bulb, and the measure of the water with the light bulb. The difference of these two measurements will be the volume of the light bulb.

In our experiment, we put the light bulb in and filled the water to read 16 oz. We then took the light bulb out and read the water level as $11\frac{1}{2}$ oz. Our light bulb took up the space of about $4\frac{1}{2}$ ounces, which gives its volume in cubic inches as

$$4\frac{1}{2} \times 1\frac{4}{5} = \frac{81}{10} = 8\frac{1}{10}$$

So, the volume of our light bulb is about 8 cubic inches.

Geometry volumes Although it is hard to find examples around your house, you can also tie in the material from Section 6.20: *Volumes and surface areas* in the *Geometry* Chapter. For example, measure the diameter of a ball, and use that to find its volume. Measure the volume of a rectangular box, and discuss how big a sphere would need to be to have about the same volume.

7.4 Weight

 Learning how to measure and describe weights.

Practice▷ Measure weight with postage or kitchen scales, bathroom scales, or a balance beam.

If you are in the United States, you may not have easy access to a metric scale, and that is fine. Practice ounce measurements by weighing letters and packages, and calculating the postage.

For examples of pounds, weigh heavier things, the most interesting being your child's weight. For comparison, weigh other family members and pets.

Your child may enjoy finding out that one American liquid ounce of water weighs very close to one ounce (in England, one imperial fluid ounce of water weighs exactly one ounce). While this works well for water, one liquid ounce of a fluid with higher density may weigh quite a bit more than an ounce.

The metric world is not as confusing. By definition, one milliliter of water weighs exactly one gram.

7.5 Temperature

Learning how to measure and understand temperature.

 Air temperatures Old-style room or outdoor thermometers, which have a colored fluid moving in a tube, can act as number lines for your child.

The two commonly used temperature scales are named after scientists from the early 1700's—German physicist Gabriel Daniel Fahrenheit and Swedish astronomer Anders Celsius.

As with other kinds of measurements, work with both the Fahrenheit and Celsius systems. You can even include the Kelvin system if your child is very interested.

There are a few key temperatures your child should learn to use for comparison with other temperatures.

- Water freezes at 32°F and 0°C.
- A pleasant indoor temperature is about 72°F and 22°C.
- Typical body temperature is $98\frac{6}{10}$°F and 37°C.
- Water boils at 212°F and 100°C.

Looking at weather reports for your local area, as well as around the country where friends or family live, is a great way to introduce your child to temperatures. Compare the different temperatures you encounter with your child. Have your child understand which temperatures feel cold, comfortable, or hot.

Converting between C and F The Celsius scale ranges from 0°C to 100°C while the Fahrenheit scale ranges from 32°F to 212°F. This means the Celsius scale increases 100 degrees per 180 degree change of the Fahrenheit scale. So, the Fahrenheit scale must change $\frac{180}{100} = \frac{9}{5}$ as quickly.

> **RULE** The conversions between C and F are
> $$F = \frac{9}{5} \times C + 32 \quad \text{and} \quad C = \frac{5}{9} \times (F - 32)$$

Since $\frac{9}{5}$ is close to 2, once your child knows a particular conversion it can be used for approximations of nearby conversions.

For example, suppose you want to convert 26°C, and your child remembers that 22°C is 72°F. Since 26°C is 4° greater than 22°C, then an approximate conversion is to add 2×4 degrees to 72°F to get 80°F.

Body temperatures Discuss the usual body temperatures for healthy, slightly sick, and very sick people. Describe the temperatures with tenths to avoid decimal numbers for now. For example, describe 98.6°F as $98\frac{6}{10}$°F.

Wall thermometers Put a big drawing of a thermometer on the wall. Mark some important or interesting temperatures on it for reference. In addition, tape paper arrows to the wall thermometer to indicate each day's high and low temperatures.

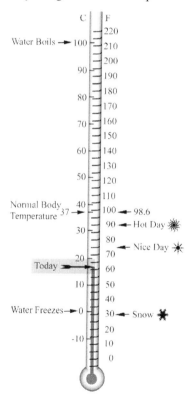

7.6 Time

LESSON

Learning how to measure and calculate time.

Practice ▶ **Skills from the first book** The first book in this series covered reading digital clocks and analog wall clocks. It described times, such as 2:32, as 32 past the hour, or as 28 before the next hour. It also went over the use of phrases such as "quarter past" and "half past."

That book also discussed that there are 7 days in a week, about 30 days in a month, and about 365 days or 52 weeks in a year. It also described how to remember the number of days in each month.

Calendars Almost all people today use the Gregorian calendar, or a calendar from one of the religions. The calendars all seem to have a lunar cycle basis, so they have years with about 12 months and the months are approximately 29 or 30 days long.

It is very difficult to make a simple calendar system for a year that is approximately $365\frac{1}{4}$ days long and a lunar cycle of about $29\frac{1}{2}$ days. Investigate the different calendar systems and see how different cultures have tried to solve this problem. Here are the names of some of the more prominent systems: Babylonian, Egyptian, Chinese, Hebrew, Christian, Hindu, Islamic, Roman, Julian, and Gregorian.

Different units The units of time larger than a day are: week, month, year, decade (10 years), century (100 years), and millennium (1,000 years).

Children usually enjoy learning about leap years. The rule is that there is a leap year of 366 days every four years, except that there is no leap year every 100 years that is not a multiple of 400.

The units of time less than a day are: hour, minute, second, millisecond (thousandth of a second), microsecond (millionth of a second), and nanosecond (billionth of a second). To help your child get an idea how short one nanosecond is, it is about the length of time it takes light to travel one foot. Microseconds and nanoseconds are important units in working with computers.

Time of day Some schedules use 24 hour time. In this system, midnight is 00:00, noon is 12:00, and 1 second before midnight is 23:59:59.

Most of us use 12 hour time, annotating times in the morning with "a.m." and times in the afternoon and evening as "p.m." Note that 12 a.m. is midnight, and 12 p.m. is noon. There is enough confusion about this that it is usually clearer to say 12 midnight or 12 noon.

The abbreviation a.m. stands for "ante meridiem," which means before midday. The abbreviation p.m. stands for "post meridiem," which means after midday.

Time zones Talk about how it should be about noon for you when the sun is as directly overhead as possible. Since the sun can only be overhead in one area of the globe at a time, it cannot be noon everywhere at the same time. This inspired people to break the earth into time zones. Most time zones are 1 hour apart, so the earth is broken up into 24 major time zones.

Time zones are based on *meridians*, or *lines of longitude*. Meridians are circles that go around the globe through the north and south poles. They are described in terms of degrees from the *prime meridian*, which is the meridian that goes through a famous observatory in Greenwich, England. There are 360° for 24 time zones, so each time zone is 360° ÷ 24 = 15° wide.

Roughly speaking, the time zones are centered on the meridians that are 15° apart. Greenwich Mean Time, or GMT, is the time zone centered on the prime meridian. Looking at the map, ask your child why the time zone boundaries are such jagged paths.

If you have relatives or close friends in other time zones, discuss what time it is for them when you call them. Talk about why it may be a bad idea for you to call them when it is late evening or early morning for you.

When you take airplane trips, look at the scheduled take-off and landing times. Talk about why the duration of the flight is not the same as the difference of the landing and take-off times. This is particularly interesting for those westward flights whose landing time looks to be before the take-off time.

The interested child may enjoy investigating the many unusual time zones that exist in various places. For example, China decided it was simpler to have only one time zone across its entire country. Your child can also look into the strategies adopted in the United States for areas near the western or eastern edge of a time zone. The international dateline, the boundary in the Pacific Ocean where the time zones change from one day to another, is also a fun topic to learn about and explore.

Duration problems There are two tricky aspects that duration problems can have.

2 time zones If a problem involves two time zones, convert all of the times to one time zone.

For example, suppose a flight leaves Los Angeles, California, at 7:00 a.m. PST (Pacific Standard Time), and arrives in Boston, Massachusetts, at 3:30 p.m. EST (Eastern Standard Time). Find the flight duration by converting one of these times to the other time zone. For example, the arrival time in Boston is 12:30 p.m. given in PST. Now that the two times are expressed in terms of the same time zone, the time difference between 7:00 a.m. and 12:30 p.m. is 5 hours and 30 minutes.

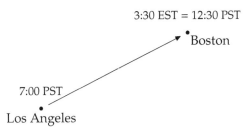

Crossings Another problem that can occur is when the time interval crosses time boundaries. If a time crosses between a.m. and p.m., or crosses from one day to the next, the calculation requires a little more attention.

There are many ways to handle these crossing problems. As an example, find the length of time from 8:25 a.m. to 4:15 p.m.

One method is to add up the times to the crossing points. The duration from 8:25 a.m. to 12:00 p.m. is 3 hours and 35 minutes. The duration from 12:00 p.m. to 4:15 p.m. is 4 hours and 15 minutes. The total of these times is 7 hours and 50 minutes.

Another way is to break this into two steps, and focus on the difference in the hours first. From 8:25 a.m. to 3:25 p.m. is 7 hours. From 3:25 p.m. to 4:15 p.m. is 50 minutes.

Yet another way to work on this is to regroup. In a sense, a half-day must be borrowed to add 12 hours to the hours column. This turns 4:15 p.m. into "16:15 a.m." This approach, and the subtraction of 8:25 from 16:15, is discussed further in Section 7.10: *Arithmetic with units*.

7.7 Rates

 LESSON   Learning to measure and understand rates.

Practice▷   There are a great many different kinds of rates. A few of these can be measured directly with instruments around the house, but most of them are calculated from two other measurements.

Direct measurements Speed or velocity is usually measured in miles or kilometers per hour. Your child can learn about speed by watching your car's speedometer, or by using a speedometer on a bicycle.

Pressure is a complicated rate that may be measured with available instruments. Have your child practice with a tire gauge on a bicycle or car tire to get a sense of what some typical pressures are like. The barometric pressure is usually reported on the pages of weather information, and it is also measured on many home weather systems that you can buy.

Calculated measurements Density, which is weight (mass) per volume, is a rate most children enjoy. Differences in density explain why helium or hot-air balloons rise, why bubbles rise in water, and why some liquids float on others.

There are a great many rates that involve time. Average speed is the most common, but there are others.

Acceleration is the change in speed divided by the time. For example, if you take 10 seconds to increase your car speed from 50 to 60 mph, that is an average acceleration of 1 mph per second.

Change in ice mass over time is a topic connected with global climate change. A typical unit used to measure ice loss is cubic kilometers per year.

RELATED
      This topic builds on the material covered in Section 2.7: *Distance and speed problems* and Section 2.8: *Rate problems*.

7.8   Metric names

LESSON | Learning the metric naming system.

Practice ▷

The metric system of units, also called the International System of Units, is a wonderfully logical system for describing scientific units. The metric names build on the basic names such as meter, liter, and gram. Prefixes are used with these names to create units that are multiples of these basic units.

For example, the prefix "kilo" means 1,000. From this kilometer is 1,000 meters, kiloliter is 1,000 liters, and kilogram is 1,000 grams.

Here are the standard prefixes used in the metric system.

Factor	Prefix	Symbol
10^{12}	tera	T
10^9	giga	G
10^6	mega	M
10^3	kilo	k
10^2	hecto	h
10	deka	da
$\frac{1}{10}$	deci	d
$(\frac{1}{10})^2$	centi	c
$(\frac{1}{10})^3$	milli	m
$(\frac{1}{10})^6$	micro	u
$(\frac{1}{10})^9$	nano	n
$(\frac{1}{10})^{12}$	pico	p
$(\frac{1}{10})^{15}$	femto	f
$(\frac{1}{10})^{18}$	atto	a

The symbols in the table are used for abbreviations. For example, meter is abbreviated as "m," so kilometer is "km," and millimeter is "mm."

7.9 Conversions

Learning to make conversions between measurement units.

 Practicing conversions will improve your child's feeling for the relative sizes of different units.

Conversion to a common unit This is a necessary skill when two amounts are measured with different units, or when one amount is specified in a mix of units.

Suppose your child needs to know which weight is more: 52 ounces or 3 pounds. Your child should convert the units to a common unit, and then do the comparison. In this case, it is easiest to convert the pounds to ounces. Since 1 pound is 16 ounces, then

$$3 \text{ pounds} = 3 \times (1 \text{ pound}) = 3 \times (16 \text{ ounces}) = 48 \text{ ounces}$$

Notice that the conversion is done in a very mathematical way. The unit, pound, is replaced by something that is equal to it, 16 ounces.

There are times when a measurement is given in many different units, and a common unit is needed. For example, you may need the duration 3 hours, 34 minutes, and 47 seconds converted to seconds. Convert 1 hour into 3,600 seconds, and 1 minute into 60 seconds. This gives:

$$3 \text{ hrs} + 34 \text{ mins} + 47 \text{ secs} = (3 \times 3,600 + 34 \times 60 + 45) \text{ secs}$$

Metric conversions Converting from one metric unit to another is excellent practice for multiplying by powers of 10 and understanding place value.

For example, suppose you were converting 13 kilometers to centimeters. One kilometer is 1,000 meters, and 1 meter is 100 centimeters.

$$13 \text{ km} = 13 \times (1,000 \text{ m}) = 13,000 \times (100 \text{ cm}) = 1,300,000 \text{ cm}$$

7.10 Arithmetic with units

LESSON | Performing arithmetic with measurement units.

Practice⯈   Arithmetic problems with measurements are fairly easy when a single type of unit is involved.

When there is more than one unit, there are two general approaches. One is where all of the units get converted to a single unit before the arithmetic is done. The other approach leaves the units alone, with regrouping between the units done as needed. This is very similar to doing arithmetic with mixed numbers, and the choices and decisions are much the same.

Conversion Suppose you have the problem of finding the average duration of five events, where their total time is 3 hours, 34 minutes, and 45 seconds. The way to do this problem is to convert everything to seconds, and then divide by 5. This example, and this kind of conversion, was covered in the previous section, Section 7.9: *Conversions*.

The total time is 12,885 seconds, so the average is $12,885 \div 5 = 2,577$ seconds. To convert this back to minutes and seconds, replace one second by $\frac{1}{60}$ minutes.

$$2{,}577 \text{ secs} = 2{,}577 \times \left(\frac{1}{60} \text{ mins} \right) = \frac{2{,}577}{60} \text{ mins} = 42\frac{57}{60} \text{ mins}$$

So, the average time is 42 minutes and 57 seconds.

Regrouping All problems can be done with conversions, but that is not always the simplest method. The analogy for mixed fractions is that to add $17\frac{3}{4} + 23\frac{3}{4}$, it would be silly to convert everything to fourths to do the addition. If the mixed fraction problem were done that way, the problem would turn into

$$\frac{71}{4} + \frac{95}{4} = \frac{166}{4} = 41\frac{2}{4} = 41\frac{1}{2}$$

This involves a lot of multiplying and dividing that is not needed.

Similar logic is applied to doing the equivalent arithmetic problem with gallons and quarts. It is possible to do the problem by converting everything to quarts, but it is less work not to. To add 17 gallons and 3 quarts to 23 gallons and 3 quarts, your child needs to regroup between gallons and quarts. When adding 3 quarts to 3 quarts, the sum, 6 quarts, needs to be broken into a regrouping of 1 gallon and a remainder of 2 quarts.

$$
\begin{array}{rl}
\overset{1}{17}\text{ gals} & 3 \text{ qts} \\
+\ 23 \text{ gals} & 3 \text{ qts} \\
\hline
41 \text{ gals} & 2 \text{ qts}
\end{array}
$$

Similarly, for the following duration subtraction problem, an hour must be regrouped and turned into 60 minutes.

$$
\begin{array}{rl}
\overset{7}{\cancel{8}}\text{ hrs} & \overset{8\,9}{\cancel{2}\cancel{9}}\text{ mins} \\
-\ 3 \text{ hrs} & 37 \text{ mins} \\
\hline
4 \text{ hrs} & 52 \text{ mins}
\end{array}
$$

The main difficulty with these problems is remembering that the regrouping will usually not involve a factor of 10, the way it does for multi-digit arithmetic. In the addition problem, 4 quarts becomes 1 gallon, and in the subtraction problem, 1 hour becomes 60 minutes.

RELATED

The regrouping done when adding and subtracting fractions is very similar to the regrouping needed for unit problems. The regrouping done when adding and subtracting in different number bases also adds valuable insight into these regrouping problems.

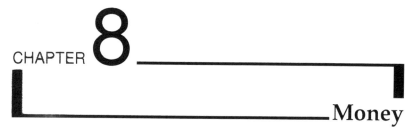

CHAPTER **8**

Money

Children have a natural interest in learning about and playing with money. Children frequently see money being used in their parents' day-to-day activities, and they see that using money causes interesting things to happen.

As one who swallowed a nickel as a child, I would like to remind you that care needs to be taken with small coins around small children, since there is a choking potential.

Introduce your child to the various coins and bills and how much they are worth. This will probably start at a very young age, so take your time. The connection between these bits of metal and paper and the value they represent is pretty abstract for a young child.

Although the examples in this chapter use the United States currency, the discussions apply with little modification to most currencies of the world.

Take advantage of your shopping errands to give your child some practice. This practice can take several forms. Sometimes your child can hand over the exact amount of money. Your child can also hand over too much money, and then check that the correct amount of money was returned. Also, if your child is going to hand over too much money, have your child think about what amount of money will reduce the change that is returned. In this last case, if the item costs $3.36 and you do not have exact change, have your child consider handing over one of $3.51, $3.56, $5.51, or $5.56.

In addition to practicing using money in shopping errands, you and your child can set up a pretend store at home. Some ideas for doing this are given in the last section of the chapter. Your home is a fun, safe environment in which to practice these skills and build up the confidence to try them in the outside world.

One way to practice with money is to have an allowance and have a "bank" with the money in it. The allowance and the bank will give practice working with money and making change. It will also give practice with learning about the relative sizes of different amounts, and how to plan to build up enough money for important purchases.

Working with money is the first exposure to decimal numbers for most children. The material in this chapter assumes that your child is not familiar with decimal numbers. I also assume that it is still a little bit early to go through all of decimal place value and arithmetic. Therefore, my approach is to use fractions and mixed numbers to explain the logic behind various monetary conversions and arithmetic.

8.1 Coins and bills

Introducing the value of coins and bills.

Practice➤ **Dollars and cents** Introduce your child to the name of each coin and its value in cents.

When your child can count to 100, introduce the one dollar bill and the dollar coins as being worth 100¢.

Money value is abstract The idea that one nickel is worth five pennies can be pretty abstract for a young child. After all, there is one piece of metal (a nickel) and another piece of metal (a penny), and it is only our symbolic understanding that tells us that they have different values.

Skip counting Skip counting with a pile of the same coin is an enjoyable way to learn the value of each coin and how it relates to others. The tactile feeling of the coins moving around and being stacked is very satisfying.

If you have a pile of nickels, have your child skip count by 5's to 100 as each nickel is pulled out of the pile. Not only does this reinforce that a nickel is 5¢, but your child will see that 20 nickels is the same as a dollar.

Adding up coins It is usually easier to add up a group of coins by starting with the coins of largest value first. For example, with a collection of 2 quarters, 3 nickels, and 2 pennies—add up the 2 quarters to get 50¢, add the three nickels to get 65¢, and finally add the 2 pennies to get 67¢.

8.2 Making same amounts of money

 LESSON | Playing a game with coins that have the same total value.

Practice▷ **Simple exchanges** For most sums of money there are many ways of putting together a group of coins that are worth that much. Use this to help teach the value of the coins, and it also provides some fun games to play with your child.

Start out with a bunch of coins on a table. Hand your child a nickel and ask to have the same value in pennies back. Do the same thing with a dime and either ask for nickels or pennies. Continue doing these simple trades to reinforce the basic value of each type of coin.

More challenging requests Over time, as your child gets better at this game, make the requests more and more challenging. For example, ask for 40¢ without using any nickels. Ask for 30¢ using exactly 6 coins in two different ways. Ask for 55¢ using the fewest number of coins.

You can find lots of interesting variations by restricting the kinds of coins used, or the number of coins used, or both.

Count the number of ways Along these lines, a challenging puzzle to ask your child is how many ways there are of coming up with a certain sum. For example, ask how many different ways there are of using nickels and pennies to come up with 13¢. Initially start out with questions that involve only two kinds of coins. After your child gets good at those questions, try some with three different coins.

This will require some well organized counting, so you will probably need to work through at least the first few together. The clearest way to organize this is to control the numbers of the larger coins and let the pennies fill in as needed.

For example, to count the number of ways of getting 20¢ with dimes, nickels, and pennies, follow the pattern in the table on the next page.

Dimes	Nickels	Pennies
2	0	0
1	2	0
1	1	5
1	0	10
0	4	0
0	3	5
0	2	10
0	1	15
0	0	20

Of course, using four or more coins gets even trickier, and is only for the very enthusiastic.

8.3 Conversions

LESSON | Learning to convert between dollars and cents.

Practice ▷ **Feeling for dollars and cents** The central idea is that there are 100 cents to a dollar.

This should be learned both as a mathematical formula, and as something your child has a feel for. Your child should have the feeling that 93 cents, or 110 cents, is close to a dollar.

Your child should also realize that one cent is one-hundredth of a dollar. So that, for example, 67¢ is the same as $\frac{67}{100}$ of a dollar.

Math for dollars and cents The main idea is to multiply the number of dollars by 100 to get an equivalent value in cents, and to divide the number of cents by 100 to get an equivalent value in dollars.

Suppose you want to convert $23.17 into cents. This is $23 and 17¢. Multiply $23 \times 100 = 2,300$ to convert dollars to cents.

$$\$23.17 = \$23 + 17¢ = 2,300¢ + 17¢ = 2,317¢$$

Of course, with just a little practice, your child will simply remove the decimal point to turn 23.17 into 2,317.

To convert 4,256¢ to dollars, divide by 100.

$$4,256¢ = \$(4,256 \div 100) = \$42\frac{56}{100} = \$42.56$$

Conversions using coins In addition to the conversions between dollars and cents, your child should also learn some standard conversions with coins.

The most common of these is that one dollar is 4 quarters, 10 dimes, or 20 nickels. There are also some others, such as that one quarter is 2 dimes and a nickel, or 5 nickels.

The game in Section 8.2: *Making same amounts of money*, which makes the same amount of money in various ways, is good practice for this.

8.4 Arithmetic

 LESSON | Doing arithmetic with money amounts.

 Practice ▶ **Whole numbers** There is nothing new if all of the money quantities are in whole number dollars, or in cents. Performing any of $12 + $56, 457¢ − 285¢, or 14 × 38¢, is simply a matter of doing arithmetic with the numbers and putting the units back in.

Introduction to decimals What is new is working with mixed quantities, such as $5.12. These numbers will probably be your child's first exposure to decimal numbers. Work with these without ever mentioning decimals, but keep it in the back of your mind that you are laying some of the groundwork.

The main task is to have your child learn why the rules for doing arithmetic with a decimal point work as they do.

There are two ways to teach this material to your child. One way is to convert $5.12 to a mixed number of dollars, $5 $\frac{12}{100}$. The other way is to convert $5.12 to whole numbers of cents, 512¢.

Either way will work, but I will use converting to cents because it is simpler and more natural. If this approach confuses your child, try converting to mixed numbers of dollars and see if that works better.

Addition and subtraction Suppose you want to add $258.37+$62.80. Eventually your child will learn to line up the decimal points, do the addition as though the decimal points are not there, and then put the decimal point in the answer. If you start with this, your child will not have any idea what is going on, and it will all be a magic spell that is easily broken.

To motivate how the decimal points work, start by converting the dollar amounts to cents. Once the problem involves whole numbers of cents, it is an easy problem. Then convert the answer back into dollars and cents.

$$
\begin{array}{r} \$258.37 \\ +\ \$62.80 \\ \hline \end{array}
\quad\Longrightarrow\quad
\begin{array}{r} 25{,}837¢ \\ +\ 6{,}280¢ \\ \hline 32{,}117¢ \end{array}
\quad\Longrightarrow\quad
\begin{array}{r} \$258.37 \\ +\ \$62.80 \\ \hline \$321.17 \end{array}
$$

When the problem is all done, point out how the dollar and cents parts of the numbers being added move straight down to the dollar and cents parts of the answer. After a few of these the pattern will be quite clear.

You can also describe why this works in terms of place value columns—single cents plus single cents produces single cents, tens of cents plus ten of cents produces tens of cents, single dollars plus single dollars produces single dollars, and so on.

Multiplication and division The approach for multiplication and division is similar to that used for addition and subtraction.

Take the problem 23 × $54.76. Start by converting $54.76 to 5,476¢, do the multiplication of whole numbers, and then convert the answer back to dollars and cents.

$$\begin{array}{r} \$54.76 \\ \times \quad 23 \\ \hline \end{array} \quad \Rrightarrow \quad \begin{array}{r} 5{,}476¢ \\ \times \quad 23 \\ \hline 125{,}948¢ \end{array} \quad \Rrightarrow \quad \begin{array}{r} \$54.76 \\ \times \quad 23 \\ \hline \$1{,}259.48 \end{array}$$

The problem $253.68 ÷ 8 is handled in a similar way.

$$8\overline{)\$253.68} \quad \Rrightarrow \quad \begin{array}{r} 3{,}171¢ \\ 8\overline{)25{,}368¢} \end{array} \quad \Rrightarrow \quad \begin{array}{r} \$31.71 \\ 8\overline{)\$253.68} \end{array}$$

With practice, the pattern of how to handle the decimal point becomes clear. The decimal point moves vertically straight into the answer.

By showing the reasoning, your child will understand what is going on, and not think it is just another arbitrary rule.

8.5   A pretend store

| Playing with a pretend store.

 You and your child can have a great time with a pretend store in your own house. Pick some favorite toys and make tags with prices on them. Find an empty box and make a cash register out of it.

Take turns being the customer and being the clerk. Sometimes, hand over too much money to the clerk, so that change will need to be made.

Making change does not need to involve any calculations. Clerks usually make change by counting up from the price of the item until the amount of money given is reached.

For example, suppose your child is given $5.00 for a 23¢ item. Your child starts at 23, and then says "24, 25" while putting two pennies in your hand, then says "50, 75, 100" while putting 3 quarters in your hand, and finally says "$2, $3, $4, $5" while putting four dollars in your hand.

CHAPTER **9**

Manipulatives

Manipulatives, things that can be looked at, handled, moved around, and manipulated, are an important part of learning for everyone. Manipulatives are especially important for young children who experience the world more through their senses, and less in intellectual ways through words and symbols.

In addition to this, people learn in different ways, and for some people it is essential to touch.

Although almost all of the manipulatives in this chapter can be bought, there are a great many that can be made at home fairly easily.

Depending on how toy-like versus how educationally oriented the manipulative is, there are several sources for buying these things. Your local toy store will have a great many of these. A teaching supply store, or a toy store that has a stronger educational orientation, will be a good source for some of these. Mail order and web-based educational supply companies will meet whatever remaining needs there are—a few of these are listed in Chapter 11: *Resources*.

9.1 Two pan balance

These provide experiences with comparing quantities and can be useful for a lot of wonderful experimentation.

One activity you can play with your child is an approximation game. Take two items which weigh about the same, and try to figure out which one is heavier by holding them in your hands. Check your guesses using the pan balance.

9.2 Volume measures

All of the various liquid and powder measuring containers you have around the kitchen will provide your child with great practice measuring things and learning about ounces, pints, quarts, teaspoons, and tablespoons (milliliters and liters if you are using metric). Obviously, any heavy or breakable containers will probably not be appropriate for your child.

9.3 Measuring devices

Gather together a collection of devices that you feel comfortable letting your child play with, and possibly break.

Measure length with rulers and yardsticks. Also, put a length scale vertically on a special section of wall, and have fun measuring your child's height every few months.

To measure small weights, pick up an inexpensive postal scale or kitchen scale. For larger weights, a bathroom scale works well.

Measure daily temperature using an outdoor thermometer that is easy for your child to see. A fever thermometer, providing daily temperature readings for family members that can be graphed, is one device that your child should not use alone.

A weather station with a thermometer, humidity sensor, and barometer is a lot of fun. Graph daily readings and make predictions about when storms are coming or leaving.

9.4 Graph paper

This is useful for making line and bar graphs, and for plotting points in a coordinate plane. Graph paper can also be used to find areas. Draw a figure on graph paper, and find the area by counting full and partial grid squares that are included in the figure. The grid points can also be used to draw figures and designs. This can be a good way to experiment with unending patterns that cover the whole paper (called tessellations).

9.5 Geometry devices

A ruler for drawing and measuring straight lines, and a protractor for measuring angles, are quite useful. In addition, a compass for drawing circles can be a lot of fun to play with. Since a compass usually has one end with a very sharp point, you will want to make sure you are with your child when the compass is being played with.

Another way to make circles, especially larger circles, is to tie a pencil or piece of chalk on the end of a string. Tie or hold the other end of the string at a fixed point (which will be the center), and draw a circle whose radius will be the length of the string.

9.6 Geoboard

Geoboards are flat boards that have pegs sticking up in a regular pattern. Usually the pattern is the grid points in a rectangular grid, but you can find other patterns as well.

Children can make lots of interesting shapes by stretching a rubber band around the pegs. It is also easy to explore the effect of various changes by lifting the rubber band off of one or two of the pegs and moving it to other pegs.

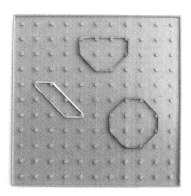

9.7 3-dimensional construction kits

There are several construction sets available in educationally oriented toy stores or on the web.

The Klikko construction sets, made by Kydko International, are one of my favorites. These sets make it easy to create regular polyhedra. Once you get used to the way the edges snap together, you can build some complex shapes very quickly. However, this snapping action can be frustrating to master for younger hands.

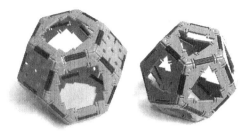

There are several other excellent construction sets available.

Polydron, by Polydron International Limited, uses plastic polygon pieces that are very similar to Klikko pieces. The way the pieces snap together appears to be simpler than the Klikko pieces, but they are also more expensive.

Zometool, by Zometool Inc., uses plastic sticks of special lengths that snap into stiff plastic connecting balls, which produce stick figures with balls at the corners.

D-Stix is similar to Zometool. D-Stix uses plastic or wooden sticks of various lengths with flexible joining corners that accept as many as eight sticks.

Another way to produce 3-dimensional shapes is to make them out of stiff paper using patterns. There are books that have patterns printed on stiff paper ready to cut out and glue. Alternatively, find these patterns in books or on the web, draw them on stiff paper yourself, and then cut them out and glue them together. The larger shapes can be time consuming and tricky to put together, but the results are very satisfying and educational for your child.

9.8 Tiling blocks

Any set of blocks where the blocks are flat and have lots of shapes can be used. Your child can use these to explore how shapes fit together, and to play with making patterns on a table or floor.

Tubs of "pattern blocks" are a good resource to have on hand. They usually contain a large number of repeated brightly colored tiles in simple shapes. These can be found in educational supply catalogues as well as some toy stores.

Pentominoes consists of 12 flat shapes, where each shape is made up of five squares put together in various configurations. Although the pieces come as part of a game to make specific challenge shapes, they can also be used by your child in free play to experiment with making original designs.

Similarly, a Tangram set consists of seven pieces of a cut up square. It comes as part of a game to make specific shapes, but the pieces, especially if you have more than one set, can be used in free play to make patterns of your child's choosing.

9.9 Calendars

Large paper monthly calendars that you can buy in bookstores or stationary supply stores work well. You can also make large ones by hand pretty easily.

In addition to paper calendars, you can buy plastic coated patterns for a calendar month that you can write on with dry-erase markers.

Sunday	Monday	Tuesday	Wednesday	Thursday	Friday	Saturday
Sun.	Mon.	Tues.	Wed.	Thurs.	Fri.	Sat.

Whichever type you use, place it in a location where your child can easily reach it and be involved with keeping track of the days and any upcoming special events or holidays.

9.10 Clocks

There are three main choices for clock faces your child can play with for reading times and setting times.

You can get a large, cheap clock that has the minutes marked on it. Besides being potentially breakable, the main drawback these often have is that the setting mechanism may involve little dials or other devices that are difficult for little children to use.

You can get what are called "Judy Clocks" of various sizes. These are sturdy clocks designed for educational use. The hands of the pictured Judy Clock can be moved independently, and it is quite simple. You can also get Judy Clocks whose minute hand causes the hour hand to move using large visible gears. If you use a clock whose hands move independently, be careful to put the hour hand in an appropriate position for where the minute hand is.

9.11 Money

The only consideration is whether your child is too small to play safely with real coins. If your child is too young, most toy stores and educational supply stores have larger plastic coins that are more appropriate.

9.12 Virtual manipulatives

Put the string "virtual manipulatives math" into a search engine and you will find a variety of wonderful and interesting sites. These include sites that feature various educational manipulatives to be played with and experienced on a computer, as well as interesting articles discussing the educational value of using these sorts of manipulatives.

Very strong among those is the site for *National Library of Virtual Manipulatives* produced by Utah State University. This site contains virtual manipulatives separated by grade level and also by the categories: Number and Operations, Algebra, Geometry, Measurement, and Data Analysis and Probability.

CHAPTER **10**

Learning Games and Activities

Sprinkled throughout this book are various games, activities, and exercises that give practice and fun with different aspects of mathematics. These activities are collected here, together with similar activities, for easy reference. Use the ideas in this chapter on an afternoon when you are looking for a new mathematical game to play with your child.

I have divided the activities into four categories for organizational purposes.

1. Logic or patterns

2. Problem solving

3. Geometry

4. Traditional commercial games

10.1 Logic or patterns

These activities all involve a logical puzzle to solve, or a pattern to understand. They do not need to involve working with numbers.

Quarto!

This game is produced by Family Games. Each playing piece has four characteristics—square or round, light or dark, short or tall, and solid or hollow. The board is a 4 by 4 grid. The players try to place a fourth piece in a row, column, or diagonal, so that the four pieces have at least one characteristic in common. It is a lovely game using characteristics and patterns.

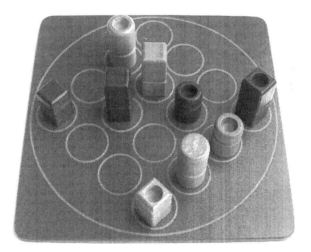

Set

This game is produced by Set Enterprises, Inc. The game consists of a deck of cards.

Each card has some symbols on it. A card has the following four features: 1) (Symbols) the symbols on it are all ovals, squiggles, or diamonds, 2) (Color) the symbols are all red, green, or purple, 3) (Number) there are one, two, or three symbols, and 4) (Shading) the symbols are all filled in, outlined, or striped.

A "set" consists of three cards with the property that each of the four features is either completely different or entirely the same. For example, in the set pictured above, the three cards have three different symbols, the cards have the same color, they all have two symbols, and they have three kinds of shading.

There are several rules for how to play, but my description should give you an idea of the pattern matching involved. This game can be enjoyed by very young kids, and can be played well by kids as young as 4 years old. It can also be quite challenging and enjoyable for adults.

Rush Hour

The game *Rush Hour, Traffic Jam Puzzle* by ThinkFun contains 40 puzzles that involve shuffling around small plastic cars and trucks on a small grid. The puzzles range in difficulty from quite easy to extremely difficult.

The puzzles are logical problems that are good for very young children in that they are oriented toward being touched and felt and require no numeric skills. There are several products similar to Rush Hour made by ThinkFun, and the series is quite popular.

Patterning and sequencing games

These can be done with shapes, drawings, objects, or numbers. The idea is to make a game out of putting several things down in a row and having your child figure out what the next one or two things should be to follow the pattern. This game is described in more detail in Section 3.3: *Patterns* in the *Reasoning* Chapter.

Towers of Hanoi

This puzzle consists of three poles and a set, usually 8, of different size disks that fit onto the poles. The game starts with all of the disks arranged in order of size placed around one of the poles. The goal is to move all of the disks to another pole. There are two rules for moving the disks: you may only move one disk at a time, and a disk may not be placed on top of a smaller disk.

For early exploration of the puzzle, remove most of the disks and have just 3 or 4 of them. After playing with small numbers of disks your child will start to sense the pattern of movement and be able to apply it to larger numbers of disks.

This puzzle provides practice with comparing sizes and counting small numbers of objects. A child can enjoy playing around with it without having to solve the whole puzzle.

10.2   Problem solving

These activities all involve solving a problem that is an equation in disguise. They are playful ways to introduce your child to this kind of problem solving.

I'm thinking of a number

A version of this game is discussed in Section 1.1: *I'm thinking of a number* in the *Equations and Inequalities* Chapter.

The game always starts with one person who is "it" who thinks of a number, and the "guesser" who tries to guess the number. Here are a few versions of the game. You may think of a different version your child particularly likes.

Comparing "It" starts by saying the number is in some range—say from 1 to 100. Then the guesser starts guessing numbers. Each guess is answered with "too big" or "too small" or "you got it." Encourage your child to learn the best numbers to guess to get the answer quickly.

Math facts "It" says "I'm thinking of a number and it is the same as 24 plus 31." Then the guesser says "is your number 55?"

Beginning equations "It" says "I'm thinking of a number and my number is 21 more than 18." For variety, this can be switched around so your child gets used to different phrases. For example, "I'm thinking of a number, and 18 is 21 less than my number."

Division "It" starts by saying the number is in a range. There are two ways of playing this version. One way is where the guesser asks questions of the form "Is your number divisible by __?" The other way is where the guesser asks questions of the form "What is the remainder when your number is divided by __?" In both ways of playing, the number used for the division is usually restricted to being less than 10.

The bag game

The bag game is an idea of educator Rick Garlikov, and is discussed at the beginning of Chapter 1: *Equations and Inequalities*. It is similar to the "I'm thinking of a number" game.

You can make the bag game variations as tricky as your child can handle. It has the potential to become quite a bit more complicated than the "I'm thinking of a number" game. As your child gets more involved with it, take turns with your child for who asks the questions and who answers them.

The game always starts off with "I have a bag and you have a bag," and ends with the question "How many are in each bag?" In the middle you can do all sorts of variations. Here are some examples:

1. I have a bag and you have a bag. We have the same number of things, and together we have 10. How many are in each bag?

   This is solved by realizing that there are two equal numbers that add up to 10. So, each bag must contain 5 things.

2. I have a bag and you have a bag. You have twice as much in your bag as I do, but if I add 4 more to my bag we have the same. How many are in each bag?

   When 4 things are added to one bag its total is doubled. So, one bag has 4 things and the other has 8.

3. I have a bag and you have a bag. You have 3 times as much in your bag as I do, but if I double mine and add 12 more I will have twice as much as you do. How many are in each bag?

   For the lesser bag, if it is doubled and has 12 added to it, then it is twice as much as what was three times it. So, four times the original amount must be 12. One bag started with 3, and the other with 9.

As you see, it can become quite complicated with just a few short instructions. If your child gets interested and plays this a lot, you will be amazed how quickly complicated questions become routine.

The bag game is very similar to two games in the book "Family Math for Young Children." This book has one game where you make salads with two kinds of beans, and another where you have a fishbowl with two kinds of fish.

For the salad game, create recipes by stating how many of one kind of bean you want in relation to the other kind of bean. For example: "This salad has 12 beans, and 5 of them are black beans, how many are lima beans?" Similar things are done with the fishbowl. For example: "There are 7 fish in the bowl, and there is one more goldfish than catfish. How many of each kind of fish are there?" You may wish to replace the bag game with one of these, or some other story that seems particularly appealing to your child.

'SMATH and Mixmath

'SMATH is made by Pressman, and Mixmath is made by Wrebbit. Both of these are scrabble-like games that use numbers and arithmetic rather than letters and words.

Missing number puzzles

These puzzles are made using underlined spaces to represent a single digit in a multi-digit problem. Create these by starting with a problem with all of the digits, and then remove a few of the digits. Check the problem before giving it to your child, to make sure you did not remove too many digits!

Here is an example:

$$
\begin{array}{r} 23 \\ + 36 \\ \hline 59 \end{array}
\quad \Rrightarrow \quad
\begin{array}{r} \_3 \\ + 3\_ \\ \hline 59 \end{array}
\quad \text{or} \quad
\begin{array}{r} 2\_ \\ + 36 \\ \hline \_9 \end{array}
$$

There is a longer description, along with more examples, in Section 1.3: *Using blank spaces* in the *Equations and Inequalities* Chapter.

Letter substitution puzzles

A letter substitution puzzle is an arithmetic problem in which some of the digits have been replaced by letters. It has three rules.

1. A letter represents the same single digit throughout a problem.

2. Different letters represent different digits.

3. No number can have a "0" for its leftmost digit.

Here are a few examples. There is a longer description, along with more examples, in Section 1.4: *Letter substitution puzzles* in the *Equations and Inequalities* Chapter.

9	a	b	b	a	a	d
$+\ 4$	$+\ 5$	$+\ 8$	$+\ b$	$+\ a$	$+\ 2$	$+\ 2$
$a\,b$	9	c	8	$c\,4$	$b\,c$	$c\,c$

Nim

There are many variations of this two-player game. Start at 0 and pick a target number, say 12. On each turn a player has a choice of adding 1, 2, or 3 to the current total. The first player to reach the target number wins. For young children uncomfortable with numbers, use a pool of 12 raisins instead. Practicing with small target numbers, children will discover that there is a strategy to the game.

Here are some possible variations (you may invent many more):

• The player that hits the target number loses.

• Instead of using the range 1 to 3, use 1 to 4, or some other range.

• Play the game in reverse, where you start with a number, say 12, and work your way down to 0.

• Trickier variations use more than one number. For example, start with two numbers such as 7 and 9. At each turn subtract 1, 2, or 3 from only one of the numbers, until both are 0.

10.3   Geometry

These activities involve geometry and spacial visualization, and very little if any work with numbers.

Views of block models

In this game you draw the views from two (or more) viewpoints and your child tries to figure out what the shape is. The easiest shapes to do this with are ones made out of little cubes. You can make your shapes from blocks or sugar cubes to help you, but do not let the other person see your model.

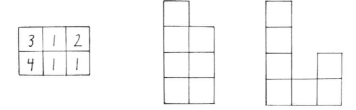

Start by making a model, either out of blocks, sugar cubes, or in your mind. In the illustrations above, the leftmost drawing shows a model of a possible set of blocks. In this example, the base is 2 by 3, and each number represents how high the blocks are above that square of the base.

After you have your own model, draw two views of it for the other person. Often these will be the view from the front and from a side, but you can also do top or bottom views. Normally, the views do not show shading or shadows to indicate depth, but vary the rules depending on what seems fun and challenging. The other person will then draw one of the missing views or create a block model.

There will be many occasions in which the front and side views are consistent with more than one model. So, just because your models are not the same does not mean that anything is wrong.

Sprouts

This is a popular geometry game that you can play anywhere you have something to draw on. This game was invented by John Conway and Michael Paterson in 1967.

Start by marking just a few spots anywhere on a piece of paper— usually 2, 3 or 4 dots are plenty. A move consists of adding a curve drawn between two spots, or a loop starting and ending at a single spot. A new spot must be added somewhere along this new curve or loop. The new curve or loop cannot cross or touch any earlier curves and loops. No spot can have more than three connections to it, where a loop counts as two connections. You win if your opponent has no legal move.

The simple game shown started off with two spots, A and B. I have added numbers on the dots to show the order in which they occurred. The first move connected A and B and added the dot labeled 1. The next move created a loop at A and added the dot labeled 2. This is the stage of the game shown in the first illustration. After three more moves there were no more legal moves, so the game was over.

Changing the maximum number of legal connections from three to four, or even higher numbers, provides some variation, but I have not tried it.

A good way to look at this game is in terms of what are called survivors. A spot is a survivor if it does not have all three connections made to it. The second player will win if the game starts with an even number of spots and ends with an even number of survivors, or if it starts with an odd number of spots and ends with an odd number of survivors. Otherwise, the first player will win. Tell your child about survivors and play with examples trying to discover the pattern.

Cube puzzle

The challenge is to use these 7 pieces to create a 3 by 3 by 3 cube. It has thousands of solutions, so it is fun to play with.

Tangram, Pentominoes, and Blokus

Tangram and Pentominoes use a set of flat shapes to create puzzles for creating flat designs. While you can make a set of either of these, you will be happier buying sets from a web retailer that carries them.

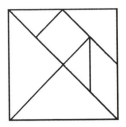

A Tangram set is a square cut up into seven pieces—five triangles, a square, and a parallelogram. Pentominoes consists of 12 figures, each a different shape using five squares. The game is to create a specified challenge shape with some or all of the figures in the set. A set of challenge shapes comes with each set, but you can also find these shapes by looking on the web, or by creating your own.

There are many commercial games in which opponents fit pieces together to form shapes or block an opponent. Blokus, made by Mattel, uses pieces similar to Pentominoes pieces, and stands out in this group.

10.4   Traditional commercial games

Quite a few of the traditional games that children play involve practice with math facts and how numbers fit together. As children get more sophisticated, they can start forming strategies by using the probabilities that different rolls of the dice will occur.

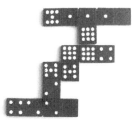

The games of Sorry, Dominoes, Aggravation, and Chutes and Ladders are good starting games that involve simple counting or matching. Similarly, the card games Go Fish, Rummy, and Solitaire can be played at a basic level of counting and matching.

The games of Parcheesi, Cribbage, Blackjack, and Backgammon are a little more difficult, but they are well within reach of children who have learned basic adding facts.

CHAPTER 11

Resources

This chapter contains brief lists of books and other resources that you may find helpful in doing math with your child. For each item I have included a brief description of what it contains and what I found interesting about it.

These lists cannot possibly be exhaustive, and they are nearly impossible to keep up to date. You should consider this as a starting point from which you may find many additional useful resources.

11.1 Reading books with math

Use these books to provide pleasant experiences that involve mathematics that you can share with your child. Though these books have various math themes that can be learned or practiced, that is not what I consider to be the most useful aspect of the books. Rather, by reading these books together you are building up experiences of math being a cozy, happy thing to do together.

Many of these books are part of a series, but there are also a great many good books outside those series. It may be hard to find many of these books at local bookstores, but they are relatively easy to find on the internet at online stores such as Amazon.com.

MathStart (book series) by Stuart Murphy.

This is a popular series of 32-page children's picture books, aimed for children from ages 3 to 10. Each one has a simple story that teaches a basic math concept along with a social skill such as sharing. The books are organized in three levels, covering math topics from beginning counting and ordering, up through multiplication, division, and building equations.

Math Mysteries by Jack Silbert (Scholastic, 1995).

This contains 20 stories that are simple mysteries using some elementary math concept. Each story is followed up with a short sequence of about five similar math questions to solve. The skill range is for grades 2 to 5. It is designed for a teacher to use in a classroom, but it is easily used by a parent with a child. If your child enjoys the stories, it can offer nice motivation to practice the math concepts.

In addition to these two series, I found, but have not reviewed, the following series: "Hello Math Reader," "Anno's Math Games," and "Pig's Math."

The Greedy Triangle by Marilyn Burns (Scholastic, 1994).

This is a charming short story for young children under the age of 9 or so. It is a good introduction to the basic polygon shapes. It describes a triangle that is unhappy with his shape, and so he tries out having the shape of various polygons. The story describes examples of how each shape is found in the world.

The Man Who Counted, a collection of mathematical adventures by Malba Tahan (W. W. Norton and Co., 1993).

This is a translation of stories with a strong Islamic theme origi-nally told in 1895. It describes the adventures of a man who was very good at counting and solving mathematical puzzles. The adventures are well told, and the math puzzles are explained at a level for a child in grade 4 or higher.

The Number Devil, a mathematical adventure by Hans Magnus En-zensberger (Henry Holt and Company, 1998).

This is the story of a boy who has trouble sleeping and who does not like math. A number devil starts visiting the boy in his dreams posing various interesting math puzzles to him. In a sequence of 12 dreams the boy learns to enjoy the puzzles, and he also starts sleeping better. The puzzles and stories are at a level for a child in grade 4 or higher.

11.2   Books for parents and teachers

These books give instructions, ideas, guidelines, and help for parents
and teachers wanting to teach some aspect of math to children. I
am also including, at the end of this section, references to a few of
the many academically backed math education programs that have
been created at colleges and universities. I have omitted the purely
teacher-oriented books, in that they are targeted at classroom and
group situations.

Math Coach, A Parent's Guide to Helping Children Succeed in Math
by Wayne A. Wickelgren and Ingrid Wickelgren (Berkley Books, 2001).

> This is an excellent book aimed at showing a parent how to
> help reach a child's full math potential. Lots of ideas are given
> for improving your child's math environment both in and out
> of school. Half of the book covers a quick course on how a
> parent can teach their children basic aspects of mathematics from
> beginning arithmetic up through algebra.

Math for Your First- and Second-Grader by Steve Slavin (John Wiley
and Sons, 1995).

> Slavin's book is probably the book most similar to my series of
> books. It is an excellent book designed for parents helping their
> children learning beginning mathematics. It starts with basic
> counting, and works its way through to counting to 1000, basic
> fractions, clock reading, and multi-digit addition and subtraction
> with regrouping. It does not do much with multiplication and
> division.

Helping Your Child with Mathematics (Grades K–2) and *Helping
Children with Mathematics (Grades 3–5)*, by James Riley, Marge
Eberts, and Peggy Gisler (Good Year Books, 1993 and 1996 respec-
tively).

> These are some of the best guides giving a progression of learning
> steps and activities for parents teaching beginning math concepts
> to their children.

Bringing Math Home, a parent's guide to elementary school math by Suzanne L. Churchman (Zephyr Press, 2006).

> This is a book of elementary school math topics presented as lessons for parents to use with their children. The book is organized around the ten National Council of Teachers of Mathematics standard areas of math. Each topic is presented with a description, an activity that can be done in the home, and a children's book that can be read with your child. The book has a very good collection of activities and explorations for children. However, the math is not broken down into a progression of simple learning steps.

Beyond Facts & Flashcards—Exploring Math With Your Kids by Jan Mokros (Heinemann 1996).

> This book is full of interesting games and activities designed to involve children in fun math experiences in a family atmosphere. A lot of examples are given involving children in using math to analyze problems in their daily lives.

Math Matters by Suzanne H. Chapin and Art Johnson (Math Solutions Publications, 2000).

> This is an excellent book, intended for teachers, which gives a deeper look at the concepts for teaching basic math from counting up through starting geometry and algebra. It is not a step-by-step guide for the teaching of this material to children, but it has a wealth of good ideas and insights.

What Your 1st Grader Needs to Know edited by E. D. Hirsch, Jr. (Doubleday, 1991).

> This is the first in a series of six books that covers first through sixth grade. These books give a thorough description of the material they think your child should know in every area of schooling for a given grade. The math sections are reasonably detailed and provide a good progression from grade to grade.

Math to Learn (Grades 1–2) by Mary C. Cavanagh (Great Source Education Group, 2006).
Math to Know (Grades 3–4) by Mary C. Cavanagh (Great Source Education Group, 2006).

Math at Hand (Grades 5–6) (Great Source Education Group, 2006).
Math on Call (Grades 6–8) by Andrew Kaplan (Great Source Education Group, 2004).

> These books are encyclopedic resources covering math at the various grade levels. They are densely packed with examples and detailed descriptions. They give descriptions of procedures, rather than the underlying reasons the methods work. They are handy as review notes.

handy homework helper Math by Janet Moredock (Publications International, Ltd., 1999).
Math Smart by Marcia Lerner (Princeton Review, 2001).

> These books, and many books like them, provide an outline of mathematics starting in elementary school and going into middle school. They are intended as a reminder of what each concept is, and what the associated techniques are. They are not intended as text books, and lots of details are omitted.

How to Develop Your Child's Gifts and Talents in Math by Ronn Yablun (RGA Publishing Group, Inc., 1995).

> This book presents how to teach your child basic arithmetic, time telling, decimals, and fractions. The material is done in a incremental manner, but the chapters on arithmetic are not broken down into detailed learning steps.

Mathematical Investigations—A Series of Situational Lessons—Books 1, 2, and 3 by Randall Souviney, Murray Britt, Salvi Gargiulo, and Peter Hughes (Dale Seymour Publications).

> These books use a learning-through-problem-solving approach to a variety of mathematical topics. Each topic is covered for anywhere from four to ten pages. The topic coverage is organized so that the student investigates and discovers patterns and principles. General problem strategies, such as "looking for symmetry" and "guess and check," are introduced and practiced frequently. The books are aimed at secondary school students, so they are a bit advanced for the readers of this book. However, a few of the simpler topics are within reach and are well worth the effort.

Family Math by Jean Kerr Stenmark, Virginia Thompson, and Ruth Cossey (EQUALS, 1986).

Family Math—The Middle School Years by Virginia Thompson and Karen Mayfield-Ingram (EQUALS, 1998).

Family Math for Young Children by Grace Davila Coates and Jean Kerr Stenmark (EQUALS, 1997).

101 Short Problems from EQUALS edited by Jean Kerr Stenmark (EQUALS, 1995).

Get It Together—Math Problems for Groups Grades 4–12 (EQUALS, 1989).

> These five books come from the EQUALS project. They present a wonderful problem-solving approach to learning math. The "Family Math" books are designed to be used by elementary school children and their families exploring the problems as a group. The problems and books are not presented as a step-by-step course in mathematics. They are for exploration, providing deeper learning and enjoyment of the mathematics material.

Young Mathematicians at Work series: 1. *Constructing Number Sense, Addition, and Subtraction,* 2. *Constructing Multiplication and Division,* and 3. *Constructing Fractions, Decimals, and Percents* by Catherine Twomey Fosnot and Maarten Dolk (Heinemann 2001 and 2002).

> These books are aimed at teachers, and are an outgrowth of the "Mathematics in the City" project supported by City University of New York-City College and the Freudenthal Institute of The Netherlands. The authors analyze how students learn mathematics best. They argue for guiding students to discover their own methods for solving problems and applying math to their world, what they call "mathematizing." They also suggest that math teachers become mathematicians, in a classroom of mathematicians. The books describe a great many examples of interactions with students in classrooms.

The Math Forum at Drexel University, web address: `mathforum.org`.

> This is a great resource that has a lot of activities in math education. In addition to having extensive links to math activities around the web, they have their own activities such as "Ask Dr. Math" and problems of the week.

11.3 Books teaching math subjects

These math books focus on teaching a particular area of mathematics.

the Art of Problem Solving—Introduction to Counting & Probability by David Patrick (AoPS 2005).
the Art of Problem Solving—Introduction to Geometry by Richard Rusczyk (AoPS 2006).

> These books, by my friends at the Art of Problem Solving, are natural follow ups to the associated topics covered in this book. These books are excellent textbooks that teach by using lots of problem solving. Each section is started with problems to solve that introduce the topics of the section. After working on those problems the student is presented with a running commentary on how to solve those problems and problems like them. This is followed up by more problems to work on of the same type.

Turtle Geometry, The Computer as a Medium for Exploring Mathematics by Harold Abelson and Andrea diSessa (MIT Press, 1986).

> This book uses the computer language LOGO to explore geometry, patterns, designs, logic, and many mathematical ideas. The material in Section 6.4: *Taking directions* in the *Geometry* Chapter uses the basic commands from LOGO.

> To find out about the many versions of LOGO that are available visit el.media.mit.edu/logo-foundation/. This has a list of commercial and free versions that are available.

Cut & Assemble 3-D Geometrical Shapes and *Cut & Assemble 3-D Star Shapes* by A. G. Smith (Dover Publications, 1986 and 1997).

> These books contain pre-drawn patterns that you can cut out and glue together to make 3-dimensional shapes such as cubes, tetrahedrons, and many more elaborate shapes.

Ultimate Kids' Money Book by Neale S. Godfrey (Aladdin, 2002).

> This is reputed to be an excellent book for children ages 9 to 12 to learn about all aspects of money, including its history. I have not reviewed the book.

11.4 Books of math games, puzzles, and fun

Mega-Fun Card-Game Math by Karol L. Yeatts (Scholastic, 2000).

> This has 25 card games that are for one or two players. The level of math is for grades 1 to 3. These games provide good math practice, and are mostly calculational in nature.

Sideways Arithmetic From Wayside School and also *More Sideways Arithmetic From Wayside School* by Louis Sachar (Scholastic, 1994).

> These two books are filled with letter substitution puzzles and math puzzles. The puzzles are put in the middle of engaging stories that are fun for children.

False Logic Puzzles by Norman D. Willis (Sterling Publishing Co., 1997).

> This book is filled with fun logic puzzles involving people who always tell the truth, always lie, or have other problems with telling the truth. The problems range from fairly simple to nearly impossible.

Solve This—Math Activities for Students and Clubs by James Tanton (The Mathematical Association of America, 2001).

> This book contains a fun collection of puzzles and mathematical activities.

5-Minute Math Problem of the Day by Martin Lee and Marcia Miller (Scholastic, 2000).

> This book contains 250 problems providing fresh perspectives on all of the major math content areas of elementary school. Each area has five to ten problems that are not as hard as a puzzle, but require more interesting thinking than calculating a simple drill problem.

Martin Gardner has written many excellent books of enjoyable ways of looking at mathematical thinking. They contain puzzles and new or interesting ways of looking at math topics.

11.5   Math competitions and challenges

Here are some resources relating to math competitions and challenging math problems.

The competitions given by Mathematics Olympiads in the Elementary and Middle Schools (MOEMS) consists of two levels: elementary school students and middle school students. Their website is www.moems.org.

Math Olympiad Contest Problems for Elementary and Middle Schools by Dr. George Lenchner (Glenwood Publications, 1996).
Math Olympiad Contest Problems: Volume 2 by Richard Kalman, Ed. (MOEMS, 2008).
Creative Problem Solving in School Mathematics by Dr. George Lenchner (MOEMS, 2005).

Each book contains about 400 challenging problems intended for grades 4 to 8. The first two books contain problems and solutions from the MOEMS program. The third book gives a detailed discussion of problem solving strategies, and provides interesting problems as examples of how to apply those techniques. The books are excellent resources for challenging and interesting math problems.

MATHCOUNTS is an extremely popular middle school math competition for grades 6 to 8. Their website is www.mathcounts.org.

The All-Time Greatest MATHCOUNTS Problems by MATHCOUNTS Foundation.
<yearly> MATHCOUNTS School Handbook by MATHCOUNTS Foundation.

These are books of MATHCOUNTS problems and solutions. These are suitable for grades 6 to 8. The first book contains approximately 140 problems, each of the other two contain about 300. The yearly books include an appendix of problem-solving strategies. The current year *Handbook* is free to download from the MATHCOUNTS website. These books provide excellent practice to prepare for the MATHCOUNTS competition.

The Math League provides contests once a year in the lower grades, and monthly contests in high school. Their website is `www.mathleague.com`.

Math Contests—Grades 4, 5, and 6. Volume 1 by Steven R. Conrad, Daniel Flegler (Math League Press, 1992).
Math Contests—Grades 7 and 8. Volume 1 by Steven R. Conrad, Daniel Flegler (Math League Press).
Math Contests—High School. Volume 1 by Steven R. Conrad, Daniel Flegler (Math League Press).

> There are five volumes for each level. Each book consists of the contest problems and solutions for a span of years.

The American Mathematics Competition consists of several levels of competitions. They are all a bit advanced for the age group of this book, but the youngest level, the AMC 8, has problems that may be enjoyed by some of the more enthusiastic children. Their website is `www.unl.edu/amc/`. The website sells CDs and booklets containing past year contest problems and their solutions.

The Art of Problem Solving Introduction series, mentioned in Section 11.3: *Books teaching math subjects*, contains problems and problem-solving strategies aimed at developing math competition skills.

Mathematical Challenge by Tony Gardiner (Cambridge University Press, 1996).
More Mathematical Challenges by Tony Gardiner (Cambridge University Press, 1997).

> These books contain challenging problems and solutions from the United Kingdom Schools Mathematical Challenge. The problems are designed for children of ages 11 to 15.

Challenge Math For the Elementary and Middle School Student by Edward Zaccaro (Hickory Grove Press, 2005).
Primary Grade Challenge Math by Edward Zaccaro (Hickory Grove Press, 2003).

> I have not read either of these books, but many readers speak highly of them.

11.6 Software programs

There are many mathematical software programs, and new ones come out fairly often.

Zoombinis This game gives great practice with logical skills.

> Zoombinis Logical Journey (Broderbund)
> Zoombinis Mountain Rescue (Broderbund)

Pit Droids This provides wonderful practice in finding patterns and learning how to describe those patterns. The patterns use colors, objects, and movements, and range from very easy to nearly impossible.

> Star Wars: Pit Droids (Lucas Arts Entertainment)

Mosaic Magic This is the most elegant program of the group, though it is not well known. In this program your child will play with basic, flat shapes and see how they can be rotated, reflected, and colored in. The object is to find the pattern of a drawing, and use pieces that the child constructs to fill in the missing pieces. Giving the sequence of directions for creating new pieces requires careful thought that will teach your child a lot.

> Mosaic Magic (Kinder Magic Software)

GeoGebra and The Geometer's Sketchpad These are amazing programs for playing with geometry constructions. These programs provide a wonderful freedom to try things out and see what happens when drawings are changed. The two programs have very similar capabilities, but GeoGebra is free. The student edition of Geometer's Sketchpad is reasonably priced and provides the functionality of the non-student edition.

> GeoGebra (`www.geogebra.org`)
> The Geometer's Sketchpad (Key Curriculum Press)

LOGO There are many commercial and free versions of the LOGO language. It is a wonderful language for learning basic geometry, discovering patterns, and for an introduction to computer programming. To find out about what is available a good site to visit is:

> `el.media.mit.edu/logo-foundation/`.

11.7 Educational supply companies

There are quite a few companies that sell educational materials by mail order and on the internet. They take many forms, and here is just a sampling to give you a few ideas.

Critical Thinking Books & S/W (www.criticalthinking.com)

> This company has excellent sets of workbooks and software designed for classroom or home use.

Cuisenaire (www.etacuisenaire.com)

> They sell Cuisenaire rods and other educational supplies and manipulatives for classroom or home.

Discovery Toys (www.discoverytoysinc.com)

> This company sells educational toys, books, and software. The toys are for children up to age 10 or so.

Educational Resources (www.edresources.com)

> General seller of educational software.

Key Curriculum Press (www.keypress.com)

> They carry interesting software, textbooks, workbooks, manipulatives, and mathematical exploration materials.

Mindware (www.mindwareonline.com)

> They are a general seller of educational toys for home use.

Pearson Learning Group. (www.pearsonlearning.com)

> This group contains the publishers Modern Curriculum Press and Good Year Books, which are a couple of the publishers of some of the books in this book list. It also has Dale Seymour Publications, which has a lot of mathematics material.

Summit Learning (www.summitlearning.com)

> This company specializes in math and science manipulatives for classroom use in grades K–9.

Terrapin (`www.terrapinlogo.com`)

The main item of interest from this company is its LOGO software product, which is great for learning geometry, math concepts, and beginning programming.

Visit `el.media.mit.edu/logo-foundation/` to find out about other versions of LOGO. This site has a list of commercial and free versions of LOGO that are available.

The Learning Company (`www.broderbund.com`)

They are a general seller of educational software.

11.8 Internet math resource sites

There are many helpful math internet sites. Some have math education ideas, learning games, and lesson plans; some have free worksheet or course materials that may be copied; others provide reference points to other internet math resources.

I must start off with a shameless plug for my website at www.DrWrightsKitchenTableMath.com. On this site I have gathered together an up-to-date list of resources, ideas, and discussions that you can use when looking for fresh directions for doing math with your child.

The site www.artofproblemsolving.com provides a wonderful gathering place for students interested in mathematics. The online courses offered are for students in grades 6 through 12, so that part of the site is a bit advanced for readers of this book. There are also free community chat groups for children in grades 4 through 12. The chat groups range anywhere from the whimsical to the advanced, highly mathematically focused.

In trying to draw up this list, it soon became clear that the list was vast and it changed frequently. Rather than providing an abbreviated list, here is a site to look at that maintains its own lists. Look at the "Resources and Tools" area in www.mathforum.org.

In addition to these, you can find lots of sites by using your favorite search engine (such as Google). Each of the following groups of keywords produces an interesting collection of sites: (homeschool math), (children math), (worksheets math), and (virtual manipulatives math).

11.9 Mathematics curricula

These provide extremely detailed, day-by-day, descriptions of what to teach your child, and how to teach it. They also provide work books and materials for your child to practice with.

Here are some of the main math curricula that I am familiar with: Math-U-See, Miquon Math, Saxon Math, Beka, and Singapore Math. I have left out listing mathematics curricula that are part of a general education curriculum, such as Calvert.

A good area to search to find further suppliers of this type is the area of home schooling resources.

Index

Dr. Wright's Kitchen Table Math
Books 1, 2, and 3

This three-book set is for parents who want to do math with their children. The books start with counting and cover all of elementary school math. They provide full explanations and step-by-step methods for parents teaching math to their children. They also provide games and activities to bring out the fun, joy, and everyday usefulness of math.

Book 1: Ages 2 to 8
This covers counting to 100, single-digit arithmetic, and beginning fractions. It has sections on geometry, time, measurements, probability, and graphing.

Book 2: Elementary School Math—Arithmetic
This has arithmetic for multi-digit numbers and fractions. It also has sections on number sense, the history of numbers, and playing with numbers.

Book 3: Elementary School Math—Beyond Arithmetic
This book focuses on the non-arithmetic parts of elementary school math. It covers solving equations and word problems, probability and statistics, graphing, geometry, measurements, time, money, and reasoning.

Come visit my website:
www.DrWrightsKitchenTableMath.com

This site has material for parents wishing to augment and enrich what their children are doing in school and for parents home schooling their children. It has up-to-date references to excellent sites where you can find games, activities, math problems, and discussion groups. Please visit my site and send me a question or a suggestion for a new idea—I would love to hear from you!

Made in the USA
Charleston, SC
18 April 2013